6

WORLD HEALTH ORGANIZATION
MONOGRAPH SERIES
No. 6

CARDIOLIPIN ANTIGENS
Preparation and Chemical and Serological Control

CARDIOLIPIN ANTIGENS

Preparation and Chemical and Serological Control

MARY C. PANGBORN, Ph.D. — F. MALTANER. Ph.D. — V. N. TOMPKINS, M.D.
T. BEECHER, M.D. — W. R. THOMPSON, Ph.D. — MARY ROSE FLYNN

Division of Laboratories and Research
New York State Department of Health, Albany, N.Y.

WORLD HEALTH ORGANIZATION

PALAIS DES NATIONS

GENEVA

1951

Originally published in the *Bulletin of the World Health Organization*, 1951, **4**, 151-200

NOTE

*Authors alone are responsible for views
expressed in the Monograph Series of the
World Health Organization*

CONTENTS

FIGURES

TABLES

FOREWORD

Cardiolipin was isolated through the work of Dr. Mary Pangborn and her associates in the Division of Laboratories and Research, New York State Department of Health, Albany, N.Y., details being originally published in 1942. This marked a significant advance in the search for a chemically defined antigen which would contribute to the improvement and standardization of serological tests for syphilis. Experiments since published in the world literature have shown also the greater sensitivity which can be obtained with serological reactions based on cardiolipir antigens, and the smaller number of biologically false positive reactions observed in conditions other than syphilis.

In view of the international importance of continuing the work initiated by the Health Organization of the League of Nations before the second World War on standardization of serological antigens and methods, and the possibility of developing international reference standards of cardio-lipin and purified lecithin, the World Health Organization took up this matter for study. The ad hoc Expert Committee on Venereal Diseases [1] pointed out that WHO might encourage a wider use of cardiolipin antigens and considered that the whole subject should be studied by a specially competent committee. In 1949 the newly established Subcommittee on Serology and Laboratory Aspects of the Expert Committee on Venereal Infections [2] stressed the necessity for stimulating production of cardiolipin antigens, but observed that the technical difficulties encountered in their large-scale production restricted their availability. Meanwhile the New York State Department of Health in order to secure the purity of cardio-lipin products had established, for non-commercial non-profit purposes, a protective patent for the USA. The Department suggested that WHO should supervise the international control of cardiolipin. At its second session the subcommittee [3] discussed arrangements for such international control and recommended that WHO collect and make available to health authorities and major laboratories technical information on the isolation, purification, and standardization methods for cardiolipin and lecithin and on the control of these products as a basis for the eventual establishment of international reference standards.

WHO, through its Expert Committees on Biological Standardization

---

[1] *Off. Rec. World Hlth Org.* **15**, 24
[2] *World Hlth Org. techn. Rep. Ser.* 1950, **14**, 14
[3] *World Hlth Org. techn. Rep. Ser.* 1951, **33**, 14

and on the Unification of Pharmacopoeias and the Subcommittee on Serology and Laboratory Aspects, is now engaged in establishing such international reference standards,[4] which are being deposited and maintained at the Statens Seruminstitut in Copenhagen, Denmark. The services of this laboratory will be available towards the end of 1951 and those of the Division of Laboratories and Research, New York State Department of Health, are now available to major laboratories for the control of purity of cardiolipin and lecithin of various origin. These laboratories will also check, on request through WHO, various cardiolipin antigens against the standards.

The present monograph has been prepared for WHO by the Division of Laboratories and Research, New York State Department of Health, Albany, N.Y. after agreement by the expert committees concerned that this would be a paper of international value for the preparation, chemical and serological examination, and control of cardiolipin antigens.

A further step towards the standardization of serology in syphilis has therefore been taken. Furthermore, pilot studies to establish international reference standards in the form of freeze-dried sera in durable form and on different levels of serological reactivity are also being carried out by WHO. The future availability of such reference sera to interested laboratories is expected to add significantly to the establishment of a more uniform, stable, and comparative basis for serology in syphilis in all parts of the world where work on this subject is being carried out.

[4] *World Hlth Org. techn. Rep. Ser.* 1951, **36**, 14

CHAPTER 1

PREPARATION METHODS

Cardiolipin is a phospholipid, containing no nitrogen, and possessing one acidic valency for each phosphorus atom. It occurs in tissue extracts in the form of neutral salts. The free-acid form is unstable. Cardiolipin antigens, used in serological tests for syphilis, are mixtures of sodium cardiolipin with purified lecithin and usually also with cholesterol. The usual source of cardiolipin is beef-heart muscle, but it is to be expected that the same product could be obtained from the organs of other animals.

Beef-heart lecithin was used in the first work on cardiolipin antigens but egg lecithin is to be preferred because it is much more easily purified. Comparison of the two lecithins has shown that they may be used interchangeably in antigen mixtures.

The preparation methods here described have given products of satisfactory purity and uniformity. However, since the serological properties of cardiolipin and lecithin may be affected by traces of impurities not readily detected by chemical analysis, each new lot must be tested by serological as well as chemical methods. The principles and techniques of such tests are discussed in chapters 2 and 3.

Both cardiolipin and lecithin contain unsaturated fatty acids and should therefore be protected against oxidation. Accompanying impurities in the tissue extracts are even more readily oxidized, and if oxidation of these substances is allowed to take place, as when beef-heart powder is stored in the dry state or when crude extracts are stored before being worked up, the purification of cardiolipin and lecithin becomes much more difficult. The conditions described below have been so chosen as to minimize this difficulty as far as practical. The following precautions should be observed :

(1) Avoid exposure of the lipid solutions to direct sunlight. For storage, use dark glass bottles or place bottles in a dark cupboard.

(2) In vacuum distillations, if a capillary inlet system is used, admit carbon dioxide instead of air through the capillary.

(3) Do not leave the lipids in ethereal solution for longer periods than specified.

(4) Complete the preliminary stages of purification as rapidly as possible. Once freed from the greater part of the accompanying impurities, solutions of cardiolipin and lecithin are surprisingly stable.

(5) Use only distilled water as a lubricant on any stopcocks or glass stoppers that come in contact with lipid solutions, so as to avoid contamination of the products with stopcock grease.

1.1 Reagents and Solvents

Reagents

Barium chloride ($BaCl_2$) 20% : 200 g dissolved in 1,000 ml of H_2O

Cadmium chloride ($CdCl_2$) 50% : dissolved in its own weight of H_2O

Sodium sulfate (Na_2SO_4) 5% : 50 g dissolved in 1,000 ml of H_2O

Sodium chloride (NaCl) : (1) saturated solution : about 360 g dissolved in 1,000 ml of H_2O ; (2) diluted solution : solution (1) diluted with an equal volume of H_2O

Barium hydroxide ($Ba(OH)_2$) saturated : Heat to boiling 6 g of $Ba(OH)_2$. $8H_2O$ or 3 g of the anhydrous compound with 100 ml of H_2O. Cover and allow to settle ; while still warm, decant into stock bottle.

80% ethanol reagent : To each litre of 95% ethanol add 200 ml of H_2O. Add 1.25 ml of 50% $CdCl_2$ solution per litre of the diluted ethanol. Before use in the extraction of lecithin, saturate this solution with petroleum ether by shaking the mixture vigorously in a stoppered bottle ; use enough petroleum ether so that a layer of it remains undissolved.

30% ethanol : Dilute 1 volume of 95% ethanol with 2 volumes of H_2O.

20% acetic acid : Dilute 1 volume of glacial acetic acid with 4 volumes of H_2O.

Solvents

Acetone and methanol of "United States Pharmacopeia" or "technical" grade may be used for the preliminary extractions. For all other operations solvents of the highest grade of purity should be used.

Ether should be of "chemical purity (CP) anhydrous" quality.

Ethanol denatured with 5% methanol may be substituted for pure ethanol, if necessary ; other denaturants are not acceptable.

1.2 Preliminary Extraction of Cardiolipin and Lecithin

Fresh, finely ground beef-heart is dehydrated and partially defatted by two extractions with acetone, and is then extracted once with methanol to obtain the phospholipids. The methanolic extract is precipitated successively with $BaCl_2$ and $CdCl_2$. The barium precipitate yields cardiolipin and the cadmium precipitate, lecithin.

1.2.1 *Method of extraction*

Remove most of the fat from fresh beef-hearts, grind the meat to a fine paste, and add 1.2 litres of acetone per kg. Mix thoroughly by vigorous shaking or stirring. After extraction, filter by suction and re-extract as before with 1.2 litres of acetone per kg. Although extraction at room temperature has been carried out successfully, it is preferable to conduct both the acetone and methanol extractions at 3º to 6ºC in order to minimize oxidation.

(1) *Preferred method.* Place the ground meat and acetone in a large container which may be stirred or shaken mechanically while refrigerated at 3º to 6ºC. Stir for about one hour, filter, return to the container with fresh acetone and again stir or shake for at least one hour. If it is necessary to let the mixture stand overnight, it should be thoroughly stirred or shaken before being left to stand.

(2) *Alternative method.* If a suitable mechanical stirrer is not available, a 24-hour period should be allowed for each acetone extraction. In this case, the mixture is placed in large flasks or bottles which are tightly stoppered and vigorously shaken by hand several times during the day, then allowed to stand overnight before filtering.

After the second acetone extraction, filter off the tissue powder by suction. If equipment for rapid low-temperature drying of the powder is available, the acetone may be removed in this way before the next extraction. An acceptable alternative is to extract the acetone-moist filter cake directly with methanol.

Return the tissue powder to the extractor and add 2 litres of 95% methanol for each kg of original wet weight. Stir or shake for four hours, then allow to stand overnight. If mechanical stirring or shaking is not used, the mixture should be allowed to extract for three or four days with frequent vigorous shaking.

Filter by suction. Wash the filter cake once with enough methanol to cover, letting the wash liquid stand on the cake for a few minutes before it is drawn off.

1.2.2 *Precipitation of cardiolipin*

Precipitation is conveniently carried out in large bottles — e.g., of 8-litre capacity — since the precipitate settles readily and the greater part of the supernatant solution can be withdrawn by siphoning. Add 20% $BaCl_2$ to the methanolic extract until no further precipitate forms (about 5 ml of $BaCl_2$ per litre). Allow the mixture to stand in the cold until the precipitate settles readily leaving a clear supernatant liquid ; this usually requires not more than an hour.

The barium precipitate contains cardiolipin, together with impurities. Lecithin remains in the supernatant solution.

1.3 Purification of Cardiolipin

1.3.1 *Preliminary purification*

Collect the barium precipitate by filtration or centrifugation and suspend it in ether ; at least 500 ml will be required for the material from

10 kg of minced heart muscle. Wash the ethereal suspension three times by vigorous shaking in a separating-funnel with 20% acetic acid. This removes certain water-soluble impurities and also decomposes the barium salts of acids weaker than acetic. After the acid treatment the ethereal solution should be clear. Pour the ethereal solution with constant mixing into 2 volumes of methanol containing 10 ml of 20% $BaCl_2$ per litre and shake vigorously to flocculate the precipitate. Centrifuge, redissolve the precipitate in a little ether, and pour the ethereal solution into 2 volumes of methanol. The ether-methanol supernatant contains about 50% of the total material from the original crude precipitate.

The precipitate obtained after this preliminary purification consists of barium cardiolipin mixed with salts of other strongly acidic phospholipids. There are several possible methods of separating these substances. The procedure described below is recommended for cardiolipin production because it has been found safe and reliable in repeated preparations.

1.3.2 *Separation of cardiolipin from other phospholipids*

In order to replace the barium of the salts by sodium, dissolve the precipitate in ether containing 10% to 15% of its volume of ethanol or methanol and shake the solution vigorously with about one-third its volume of 5% Na_2SO_4. Centrifuge the mixture to remove $BaSO_4$ and shake the ether layer once more with Na_2SO_4. The ethereal solution may next be evaporated to dryness and the residue dissolved in methanol ; or, if the volumes are small, it may be more convenient to pour the ethereal solution directly into 7 or 8 volumes of methanol. If this is done the mixture should be concentrated in vacuo sufficiently to remove most of the ether. Add an amount of saturated NaCl equal to 2% of the volume of the methanol solution. Chill overnight. Decant the supernatant and add 20% $BaCl_2$ to the clear methanol solution until no further precipitate forms. Vigorous shaking at this point will help to flocculate the precipitate. As soon as a clear supernatant is obtained, centrifuge, and wash the precipitate once with methanol and once with acetone.

1.3.3 *Purification of barium salt*

To the acetone-washed precipitate, add a measured volume of ether, equal to or slightly greater than the volume of the packed precipitate. Mix thoroughly. The characteristic gelatinous appearance of the barium salt in ether may not be observed at this point, owing to the presence of the acetone retained by the precipitate. Add to the mixture a volume of acetone twice that of the ether used, mix thoroughly, centrifuge, and discard the supernatant. The greater portion of the impurities is removed in this first precipitation. Further purification is achieved by repeating the precipitation from ether, in each case adding a volume of acetone equal to that of the ether used.

After the first precipitation, the precipitate should form a gel in anhydrous ether ; sufficient ether should be used so that a definitely gelatinous mass rather than a suspension is formed. A stiff gel is satisfactory ; further dilution with ether, in an effort to obtain a thin solution, is not desirable. After homogenizing the mixture as thoroughly as possible, add acetone, gradually at first, and mixing in each portion thoroughly before adding the next ; when a solid precipitate forms and the mixture is no longer gelatinous, the remainder of the acetone may be added rapidly. Centrifuge and repeat the ether-acetone precipitation until the supernatant is nearly colourless. Usually four or five precipitations are needed.

Dissolve the precipitate in ether to which a few drops of water are added, using about half as much ether as in each of the previous treatments with anhydrous ether. In the presence of water a solution rather than a gel results. To this solution add two volumes of acetone rapidly with constant mixing, and centrifuge.

1.3.4 *Conversion to sodium salt*

Dissolve the precipitate in wet ether containing 10% of its volume of ethanol, using at least 300 ml of ether for the amount of material obtained from 15 hearts. Shake the solution vigorously for five minutes with about one-third its volume of half-saturated NaCl. Repeat twice more, each time adding ethanol equal to 10% of the volume of ether, then wash twice with half-saturated NaCl alone, adding no ethanol. Dry the ethereal solution over anhydrous Na_2SO_4 ; filter, and concentrate to dryness in vacuo.

Immediately dissolve the dried material in dehydrated ethanol, warming the mixture to about $50^{\circ}C$ with vigorous shaking to facilitate solution ; decant, and repeat the ethanol treatment if there is any considerable amount of undissolved residue. A trace of insoluble residue is always encountered at this point and the cardiolipin solution is usually cloudy. This suspended matter separates slowly and after 24 hours at 3° to $5^{\circ}C$ one can usually decant a clear or nearly clear solution.

The ethanolic solution should be colourless or at most faintly yellow. The product at this stage consists of nearly pure cardiolipin.

The concentration of the ethanolic solution should be determined approximately by evaporating to dryness a small aliquot and weighing the residue. If the solution contains less than 5 mg per ml, it should be concentrated by vacuum distillation so as to contain at least 5 mg, and preferably 7 to 8 mg, per ml. The next step, precipitation with $CdCl_2$, may not be successful if excessively dilute solutions are used.

1.3.5 *Final purification*

To the ethanolic solution of sodium cardiolipin, add 50% $CdCl_2$ drop by drop until no further precipitate forms. Avoid unnecessary excess of the reagent. Chill overnight, collect the precipitate by centrifugation, and wash once with dehydrated ethanol. Estimate the volume of the precipitate by measurement of a water-blank in a similar centrifuge cup. Add an equal volume of ether, mix thoroughly, centrifuge, and discard the supernatant. Reprecipitate the cadmium salt twice from anhydrous ether with an equal volume of acetone, in exactly the same way as was done with the barium salt. Finally, dissolve in a small volume of wet ether. The clear, concentrated solution should be absolutely colourless. Add three volumes of acetone rapidly with constant mixing. Centrifuge. Convert to the sodium salt, and dissolve the latter in dehydrated ethanol, exactly as described above. There is usually a further trace of ethanol-insoluble impurity to be removed in preparing this final solution; and the solution which has been clarified at room temperature may slowly deposit a small film of insoluble matter on the glass after a few days' storage at 3° to 6°C. The clear solution may then be decanted and should remain clear on prolonged storage. This is the final stock solution from which antigen mixtures are prepared.

1.4 Purification of Lecithin

1.4.1 *From fresh eggs*

1.4.1.1 *Initial extraction.* The following directions are given in terms of quantities required for one dozen eggs, but amounts up to four or five dozen can easily be handled at one time. One dozen large eggs yield about 6 g of purified lecithin.

Separate the yolks of 12 fresh eggs and beat thoroughly, preferably in a Waring blendor. Add 200 ml of CP acetone and mix. Transfer from the blendor to a large beaker or flask, add another 400 ml of acetone, mix vigorously and filter by suction. Remove filter cake from the funnel, re-extract by vigorous shaking or stirring with about 500 ml of acetone, filter again by suction; repeat until the solid matter is a fine creamy-white powder and the acetone filtrate a pale yellow. This may require four or five extractions.

Transfer the yolk powder to a glass-stoppered bottle that may be placed on a shaking-machine, or to a flask suitable for mechanical stirring; add 800 ml of 95% ethanol and shake or stir at room temperature for half an hour. Filter by suction.

1.4.1.2 *Purification.* To the ethanolic extract, add 50% aqueous $CdCl_2$ until no further precipitate forms (about 20 ml are required). Shake vigorously and chill in ice or in the cold room with frequent shaking for at least one hour. The precipitate may be collected as soon as it settles readily, leaving a clear supernatant. Filter by suction and wash the precipitate on the filter once with ethanol and once with acetone.

Dissolve the cadmium precipitate in 100 ml of chloroform and pour the solution with constant mixing into 700 ml of 95% ethanol to which 10 ml of a 50% aqueous solution of $CdCl_2$ has been added. Shake vigorously. The precipitate is filterable as soon as it settles readily, leaving a sparkling clear supernatant. This may require repeated shaking at intervals for one-half to one hour at room temperature. Filter by suction, redissolve the precipitate in chloroform, and repeat the precipitation in exactly the same way, three times more, so that four chloroform-ethanol precipitations are made altogether.

Suspend the filter cake from the fourth reprecipitation in a mixture of about 200 ml of petroleum ether and 500 ml of 80% ethanol reagent. Shake vigorously either in a separating-funnel or in a bottle in the shaking-machine until solution is complete. Draw off the lower layer and re-extract the petroleum layer with about 300 ml of the 80% ethanol reagent, shaking vigorously for five minutes.

In order to avoid excessive losses due to solubility of lecithin-$CdCl_2$ in 80% ethanol, the amount of the 80% ethanol reagent should not be in excess of that necessary to effect extraction from the petroleum ether. The simplest way to ensure using the correct volumes is as follows :

After making two extractions as described above, measure the remaining petroleum-ether solution in a graduated cylinder, pipette 2 or 3 ml of this solution into a small weighed flask, evaporate it to dryness on a hot plate, and dry for about 20 minutes in a vacuum desiccator. Weigh the flask and calculate the total amount of dissolved solid in the petroleum ether. If this is 0.5 g or less, the extraction is considered complete. If larger amounts are present, make one more extraction using 100 ml of the 80% ethanol reagent for each gram of material in the petroleum ether.

Combine all the 80% ethanol extracts and concentrate in vacuo until the petroleum ether is completely removed ; this is accomplished by reducing the solution to about two-thirds its original volume. Concentration beyond this point is to be avoided. Chill the concentrated extract at 3° to 6^oC overnight (or preferably at -5^oC, if the lower temperature is available). The lecithin-$CdCl_2$ complex precipitates as the petroleum ether is removed, and the yield of the precipitate is increased by cooling.

1.4.1.3 *Removal of cadmium.* Filter the purified lecithin-cadmium salt by suction and remove the cadmium as follows :

Dissolve the salt in about 200 ml of chloroform, transfer to a separating-funnel, and shake vigorously for five minutes with an equal volume of 30% ethanol. Separate and wash the chloroform layer at least four times more in the same way with 30% ethanol. If emulsions form, they may readily be broken by centrifugation or sometimes merely by dilution with more 30% ethanol.

Since the cadmium is washed out in the form of $CdCl_2$, the simplest way to test for removal of cadmium is to test the dilute ethanol washing for chloride. The fourth or fifth washing should be so tested and, if any chloride is still present, the washing with 30% ethanol should be continued ; one final washing with 30% ethanol is carried out after the test is negative. For the chloride test, withdraw about 5 ml of the 30% ethanol layer ; if it is emulsified or very cloudy, centrifuge it to remove suspended chloroform, and if the ethanolic supernatant is still slightly cloudy it may be clarified by warming slightly. To the clear solution add one or two drops of 5% silver nitrate ; if no precipitate is observed immediately, let stand at least twenty minutes and observe again. If even faint clouding is noted, the 30% ethanol washing should be repeated.

1.4.1.4 *Final purification.* When the chloroform solution of lecithin has been washed free of $CdCl_2$, concentrate it to dryness in vacuo. Shake the lecithin residue in the distilling flask with about 50 ml of acetone, decant the liquid, and again evacuate to remove residual acetone.

Dissolve the lecithin in about 100 ml of ether and add 20 ml of acetone. The solution should be colourless and clear at room temperature. Refrigerate overnight at 3° to 6°C. Lower temperatures or longer standing in the cold should be avoided as the lecithin itself may begin to precipitate. The small precipitate of impurities separates in the form of a rather fine dense powder, which may be centrifuged down in a refrigerated centrifuge if desired but can usually be removed as easily by decantation and filtration in the cold room.

The ether-acetone solution, freed from the insoluble fraction, is concentrated to dryness in vacuo and the purified lecithin immediately redissolved in dehydrated ethanol.

1.4.2 *From beef-heart*

If beef-heart lecithin is used the following modifications of the preparation method are needed :

To the methanol filtrate remaining after removal of the barium precipitate of crude cardiolipin, add 50% aqueous solution of $CdCl_2$ until no further precipitate forms, and refrigerate overnight. Filter by suction and wash the precipitate once with methanol and once or twice with acetone. Dissolve the cadmium salt in chloroform and precipitate three times with ethanol containing $CdCl_2$ in exactly the same way as described above for egg lecithin. Remove the $CdCl_2$ by washing the chloroform solution with 30% ethanol, evaporate the chloroform solution to dryness, and dissolve the lecithin in anhydrous ether ; approximately 300 ml will be required for the quantity obtained from 10 kg of minced heart muscle. To the ethereal solution add one-fifth its volume of acetone, refrigerate overnight, and filter by suction on a cold Büchner funnel.

Evaporate the ether-acetone solution to dryness and dissolve the lecithin in ethanol to obtain an approximately 3% solution. Add a few drops of phenolphthalein and sufficient saturated aqueous solution of $Ba(OH)_2$ to give an alkaline reaction. Immediately neutralize the mixture with CO_2

and add a few ml of saturated NaCl ; shake vigorously to aid flocculation of the precipitate. Traces of acidic phospholipids are precipitated by neutralizing with Ba(OH)$_2$ and the voluminous barium carbonate precipitate absorbs most of the pigmented impurities.

As soon as the precipitate settles readily leaving a sparkling clear supernatant, filter the mixture—preferably by gravity—and reprecipitate the filtered solution with CdCl$_2$. Collect the cadmium precipitate and reprecipitate twice by pouring the chloroform solution into ethanol, exactly as before. Fractionate once by the petroleum-ether and 80% ethanol method, as described for egg lecithin. Remove the cadmium, dissolve the lecithin in ether, and add one-fifth the volume of acetone ; refrigerate overnight. Filter, keeping the mixture cold ; evaporate the solution to dryness and immediately dissolve the purified lecithin in dehydrated ethanol.

2. Potassium nitrate

Dissolve 25 g in 75 ml of distilled water.

3. Nitric acid (specific gravity, 1.40 to 1.42)

4. Molybdate reagent

Dissolve 50 g of ammonium sulfate in 500 ml of nitric acid (specific gravity 1.36) in a 2-litre flask. Dissolve separately in a beaker 150 g of ammonium molybdate in 400 ml of boiling distilled water. After cooling, pour slowly, with stirring, the latter solution into the acid solution. Make the reagent up to 1,000 ml, allow to stand from two to three days, and filter. Store in well-stoppered brown glass bottles in the cold room.

5. Nitric acid containing sulfuric acid

Prepare about 1,000 ml of nitric acid (specific gravity 1.19 to 1.21) by diluting 420 ml of nitric acid (specific gravity 1.40) with 580 ml of distilled water, and add 30 ml of sulfuric acid (specific gravity 1.84).

6. Ammonium nitrate, 2%

Dissolve 20 g of ammonium nitrate in distilled water. Add 2 ml of nitric acid (specific gravity 1.40 to 1.42) and make the volume up to 1,000 ml.

7. Ammonium hydroxide (specific gravity 0.90)

Dilute 1 part of ammonium hydroxide with 4 to 5 parts of distilled water.

8. Ethanol, 95%, redistilled

9. Acetone, C.P. or Merck's reagent grade

Apparatus

1. Water-bath : A convenient bath is an enamelled pail from 190 mm to 200 mm in diameter, with a nichrome wire gauze false bottom and a metal support which will hold the tubes in a vertical position.

2. Desiccator : A vacuum desiccator of about 100 mm diameter.

3. Filters : For filtering the acidified solution before precipitation of ammonium phosphomolybdate, use a filter tube approximately 135 mm long. The cup is 40-45 mm long and 8-10 mm in diameter and contains a fritted-glass plate of medium porosity. Pass the stem of the filter and a bent glass tube for vacuum attachment through holes in a No. 8 rubber stopper for filtration directly into the precipitation tube.

For filtering the ammonium phosphomolybdate use the same type of glass filter tube as above (coarse or medium) but fit the cup with a layer of acid-washed asbestos 2-3 mm thick. Pass the stem through the hole of a small rubber stopper which fits a tube 80 mm long, and from 8 to 10 mm bore. Pass the latter through a hole in a No. 6 rubber stopper which fits a 250-ml filter flask.

4. Large Pyrex test-tubes, 200 mm × 25 mm, for precipitation of the phosphomolybdate. These should be etched at 15 ml.

5. Siphon used for filtering : the siphon is made of glass tubing (4-mm external diameter) about 360-380 mm long. Bend the tubing so that the vertical parts are parallel and the angles approximately 80° and 110°. Pass the short arm (approximately 30 mm) through a hole in a small rubber stopper which fits the filter tube.

6. Feather used for final transfer of precipitate : snipe feathers may be purchased or white feathers from chickens or pigeons substituted. Secure the tip of a stiff feather with Kronig cement in a handle made from 11-mm glass tubing. Draw a capillary out to about 200 mm in length and 2 mm in external diameter, bend about 30 cm from the end, and seal the large end over a flame. Wash newly prepared feathers by letting stand overnight in acetone.

Procedure

Clean the empty or asbestos-filled filters by letting them stand overnight in concentrated H_2SO_4 containing a few crystals of sodium nitrate. Wash thoroughly with distilled water, followed by successive washings with ethanol and acetone. Clean the outside of the filters by wiping first with a square (approximately 60 mm $\times$ 60 mm) of moist cotton flannel, then with a similar sized, dry, flannel square, and dry in a desiccator for 30 minutes using vacuum. The pressure in the desiccator should not exceed 100 mmHg. Remove the filters from the desiccator to a bent-wire support and weigh immediately on a microchemical balance.

For solid samples

Weigh a sample likely to contain between 0.3 and 0.7 mg of phosphorus into a silver crucible of 15-20 ml capacity. Add 1 g of potassium hydroxide and 0.2 g of potassium nitrate. Cover crucible with a silver lid and fuse contents over a flame. Fuse any spattered material on the lid by holding the lid under side up in the microflame. Cool, then transfer the melt to a 50-ml Pyrex beaker with small quantities of hot distilled water. Make acid to Congo red paper using the nitric-sulfuric acid mixture and evaporate to about 5 ml on the hot plate. Filter by suction into the 200 mm $\times$ 25 mm precipitation tube. Wash with two successive 1-ml portions of the nitric acid mixture, then with distilled water, keeping the total volume down to 13 ml or less. Make up to 15-ml volume and heat in a water-bath to 81° — 85°C. (Place the thermometer in a tube containing 15 ml of H_2O ; this tube is placed in the bath at the same time as the samples.) Remove the tube from the bath. Without touching the side of the tube, add 15 ml of the molybdate reagent (warmed to room temperature) and rotate vigorously. Let stand a few minutes and shake again. Allow to stand overnight before filtering, or longer, if the precipitate is very small.

For solutions

Transfer to a 15-ml silver crucible a volume of the sample that contains from 0.3 to 0.7 mg of phosphorus. Add 0.2 ml (about 4 drops) of a 50% solution of potassium hydroxide and evaporate to dryness on the edge of the electric plate. Add 1.0 ml of 25% solution of potassium nitrate, stir with a rod, then wash rod with 1 ml of water, and warm slightly. Rub the sides of the crucible with a glass rod, wash with a few drops of water, and re-evaporate to dryness. Bake in the centre of the plate for 30 minutes, cool, add 0.9 g (7 to 8 pellets) of potassium hydroxide, fuse with a micro-burner, and complete as directed above.

To filter the precipitate, insert the small rubber stopper of the siphon into the filter tube ; then clamp the tube containing the precipitate to a stand, in such a position that the siphon is just above the precipitate, and draw over the supernatant liquid by suction. Siphon the precipitate over with washes of 2% solution of ammonium nitrate. Remove with a feather any precipitate adhering to the tube. The last traces of precipitate should be removed by a 95% ethanol wash followed by more ammonium nitrate solution. Remove the siphon and wash the precipitate with ammonium nitrate solution and with 95% ethanol, followed by acetone. Clean the outside surface of the filter, dry, and weigh as previously directed.

After weighing, dissolve the precipitate with the dilute ammonia water and wash the filter with 2% ammonium nitrate solution followed by 95% ethanol and acetone. Clean, dry, and reweigh as directed for the empty filter.

The difference in weight equals the weight of the precipitate. The factor is 0.01454.

Calculation

For solid samples

$$\frac{\text{Weight of precipitate (mg)} \times 0.01454}{\text{Weight of sample (mg)}} \times 100 = \% \text{ of phosphorus}$$

For solutions

$$\frac{\text{Weight of precipitate (mg)} \times 0.01454}{\text{Volume of sample (ml)}} = \text{mg of phosphorus per ml}$$

2.2.2 Determination of iodine number [92]

Reagents and special equipment

1. Pyridine sulfate dibromide : Measure 8.25 ml (8 g) of purified pyridine and 5.45 ml (10 g) of sulfuric acid (specific gravity 1.84) into separate 125-ml flasks each containing about 20 ml of glacial acetic acid.

Cool in beakers containing ice. Combine, then add 2.5 ml (8 g) of bromine dissolved in 20 ml of glacial acetic acid (reagent grade), and make up with glacial acetic acid to 1,000 ml. This reagent is approximately 0.1 N in bromine ; for use, a solution approximately 0.05 N is desired. Since the solution becomes progressively weaker on standing, owing to loss of bromine, it is best to dilute it in small quantities as required, by adding an equal volume of glacial acetic acid or somewhat less as indicated by previous titrations. Titration of 5.0 ml of the diluted reagent should require between 4.2 and 5.0 ml of 0.05 N thiosulfate.

2. Potassium iodide, 10% solution

3. Starch solution, 1%

4. Sodium thiosulfate, approximately 0.05 N, containing 1-1.5 ml amyl-alcohol per litre as a preservative. Standardize the sodium thiosulfate against the 0.1 N potassium bi-iodate. This is best done on the day when the thiosulfate is to be used ; however, when numerous analyses are to be made, standardization once a week will ordinarily be sufficient.

5. Chloroform, redistilled : add 1% of its volume of ethanol as a preservative.

6. Potassium bi-iodate, 0.1 N (3.250 g per litre)

7. Iodine flasks

8. Microburette, 5 ml, graduated in 0.02-ml divisions, supplied with a fine tip.

Procedure

Run samples in triplicate and a sufficient number of blanks to titrate at fairly close intervals during a series of titrations. Use samples containing 7 to 15 mg of total solids. In general, samples in solution should be evaporated to dryness, by placing the iodine flask containing the sample in a water-bath and admitting CO_2 to the flask during evaporation ; the flask is then cooled and the sample immediately redissolved in 2 ml of chloroform. [a]

To each sample and blank add 5 ml of pyridine dibromide reagent, stopper, and allow to stand in the dark for at least 15 minutes and not more than 1 hour.

Before opening the flask, pipette 0.5 ml of potassium iodide solution into the well around the neck of the stopper ; wash down the neck of the flask with about 2 ml of distilled water and titrate immediately with 0.05 N sodium thiosulfate.

Calculation

Subtract the number of ml of thiosulfate used for the sample (*a*) from that used (*b*) to titrate the pyridine sulfate dibromide alone (reagent blank).

---

[a] If the sample is contained in 1 ml or less of ethanol, the ethanol need not be removed before adding chloroform. An equal volume of ethanol is added to the reagent blank in this case. Larger amounts of ethanol interfere with the titration. Small amounts of acetone or ether introduce serious errors.

The difference equals the number of ml of thiosulfate equivalent to the bromine absorbed by the sample. The equivalent in terms of iodine is calculated as the iodine number :

$$\text{Iodine number} = \frac{(b-a) \times 6.35 \times 100}{\text{weight of sample (mg)}}$$

The factor 6.35 is derived from the equation :

1 ml of 0.1N $Na_2S_2O_3$ is equivalent to 12.69 mg of I_2 ;
hence

1 ml of 0.05N $Na_2S_2O_3$ is equivalent to 6.35 mg of I_2.

More dilute standard thiosulfate may be used if desired ; the factor must then be recalculated.

2.2.3 Determination of dry weight

Although theoretically simple, this requires special precautions if accurate results are to be obtained, because the dried lipid residues are rapidly damaged by oxidation and are also sufficiently hygroscopic to cause difficulties in weighing. The following method assumes the use of a semi-micro balance with a sensitivity of at least 0.05 mg. If an ordinary analytical balance is used, somewhat larger samples should be taken.

Erlenmeyer flasks of 10-ml capacity, fitted with ground-glass stoppers, are convenient for weighing the samples. The clean, dry flasks with stoppers should be reweighed accurately before each use. Before each weighing, the flasks are carefully wiped first with moist flannel and then with dry flannel or chamois-leather and are thereafter handled with forceps.

Measure into the weighed flask a portion of the solution containing from 10 to 20 mg of dissolved material. Evaporate not quite to dryness on the low heat of an electric hot-plate or under an infra-red lamp. When only a few drops of solvent remain, discontinue heating and complete the drying rapidly either by drawing a stream of air through the flask or by passing in a stream of CO_2 or N_2 through a fine-tipped pipette. Wipe the flasks, immediately place them in a desiccator over $CaCl_2$ and evacuate by means of an oil pump to a pressure of less than 1 mmHg. Leave them under the vacuum overnight.

In opening the desiccator, admit dry air through a tube filled with $CaCl_2$ or other desiccant. Insert the stoppers in the flasks immediately after opening the desiccator, allow the flasks to stand beside the balance for about 15 minutes, then weigh promptly.

Approximate determination of the total-solid content of the phospholipid solutions may of course be made more simply ; such approximate determinations are useful in following the course of a preparation but should not be used for calculating the composition of antigens or as a part of the final analysis.

2.2.4 *Preparation of lecithin samples for determination of amino-nitrogen*

Evaporate to dryness an accurately measured sample of the ethanolic solution containing about 0.3 g of lecithin; add 10 ml of 10% HCl, and boil under a reflux condenser until the coagulum first formed has taken an oily consistency. This may require 6 to 7 hours. Cool and filter the mixture, washing the filter paper with a little 10% HCl. Evaporate the solution nearly to dryness and neutralize with NaOH (50 to 60%) using *p*-nitrophenol as indicator. Immediately acidify with acetic acid. Make up the volume to 25 ml, allow the solution to stand in the refrigerator overnight, and then filter it through a dry paper. Use 5-ml aliquots of this solution for determination of amino-nitrogen by the Van Slyke method. [86]

CHAPTER 3

SEROLOGICAL EXAMINATION

In order to use a cardiolipin antigen in any serodiagnostic test for syphilis, it is necessary first to determine the optimal proportions in which cardiolipin, lecithin, and cholesterol must be mixed to give acceptable sensitivity and specificity in that particular test. Such a standardization provides an invariable formula for proportions of the components to be used in the antigen. The purpose of serological examination of freshly prepared lots of cardiolipin and lecithin is not to repeat the standardization in the above sense of determining optimal proportions. The purpose is to determine whether an antigen prepared with a new lot of a given component, cardiolipin or lecithin, gives satisfactory agreement with a reference-standard antigen in comparative tests. It is necessary to use serological tests in this way as a check on the acceptability of new lots because traces of impurities or decomposition products not detected by the usual chemical analyses may affect the serological activity. It is advisable to use both complement-fixation and flocculation tests for this purpose because lots may sometimes be found unsatisfactory in one of these techniques and not in the other.

The basic procedure in both cases is the same :

(1) preparation of an antigen mixture A_t, according to a previously determined formula, but with the new lot used instead of a reference-standard product of the same antigen component, i.e., a new cardiolipin with a reference-standard lecithin or vice versa ;

(2) comparison of this antigen with one prepared entirely from reference-standard materials A_r, in such a way as to show whether stipulated conditions of agreement or disagreement between them are met, so that the new lot may be considered acceptable or not in given respects.

The specific directions which follow have been designed to fulfil the following general requirements for the performance of such tests :

(1) The associated comparative results with a given serum specimen with each of the two antigen preparations (A_t and A_r) constitute an " observation ". The observations with different sera should ideally be independent; but, at least, the work should be distributed over several days.

(2) Each admissible observation is classed unequivocally according to prescribed criteria as either inferior or superior (conveniently called defective or non-defective).

(3) Conditions must be prescribed for accepting or rejecting a lot. For example, that in accepting we will tolerate a risk α that ϕ, which is the proportion of non-defective observations that would be encountered in protracted study, is less than p' ; likewise in rejecting a lot we take a risk β that ϕ is greater than p''. The values of p' and p'' and those of the risk-tolerances, α and β, must be stipulated.

(4) In view of the stipulated conditions it may be appropriate to apply direct-probability sequential analysis,[b] which indicates a decision at the earliest opportunity.

The universe of all possible observations that could be made in accord with a given plan and the definition of defective observation, etc., must be chosen with a view to testing for characteristics of the antigen A_r that may cause difficulty in its use. We wish to guard against excessive reactivity ; for this purpose the so-called " non-reacting " sera are used. On the other hand, we want to test the approximate comparability of reactions with " high-titre " sera.

The particular serological tests here described are those in use at the laboratory of the New York State Department of Health. It is recognized that other serological tests could be used for this purpose but it is recommended that any test so used should satisfy the following conditions :

(1) It should be thoroughly studied to determine the optimal proportions of cardiolipin, lecithin, and cholesterol.

(2) These proportions, once determined, should be adhered to ; i.e., the test should be standardized on the basis of a constant antigen formula.

(3) The variability of the test should be studied in order to establish suitable criteria so as to avoid the danger of rejecting a lot on the basis of apparent discrepancies that would not be detrimental to the intended diagnostic use.

3.1 New York State Department of Health Complement-Fixation Technique for Acceptance of New Lots of Antigen-Components

3.1.1 Glassware and apparatus

1. Pipettes : 1.0 ml graduated in 0.01 ml
    5.0 ml graduated in 0.1 ml
    10.0 ml graduated in 0.1 ml
    All these pipettes should be calibrated (error $\pm 2\%$ or less)
1a. Pipettes : 0.2 ml graduated in 0.01 ml
    1.0 ml graduated in 0.01 ml
    5.0 ml graduated in 0.1 ml
    10.0 ml graduated in 0.1 ml
2. Volumetric flasks of 50-ml capacity

---

b The fundamental ideas of direct-probability sequential systems are discussed briefly in Annex 1, page 54.

3. Beakers
4. Screw-cap brown bottles of about 25-ml capacity
5. Test-tubes, 12 mm × 75 mm, with rounded bottoms, and without lips
   Specimen-tubes, 100 mm × 16 mm
6. Graduated centrifuge-tubes of 15-ml capacity, graduated in 0.1 ml
7. Bottles or jars, wide-mouthed, of 100- to 300-ml capacity
8. Petri dishes
9. Cylinders, graduated, of 50- to 100-ml capacity
10. Test-tube racks, metal, suitable for carrying specimen-tubes (2 rows of 5 each) and test-tubes (2 rows of 5 or 6 each)
11. Water-bath : any regulated water-bath, with electric stirrer if possible, to be used at 37°C or 56°C, with submerged platform on which racks may be placed with tubes partially immersed
12. Centrifuge with carriers appropriate for test-tubes used in sedimentation of cells
13. Refrigerator : 3°-6°C
14. Photo-electric colorimeter

Note. All glassware should be clean but not necessarily sterile. Put used pipettes in water to which washing soda has been added. Empty all used bottles and rinse in tap water. Put used tubes in pails of water. Wash glassware preferably with a soapless detergent. Avoid the use of products which will cause deposits of calcium from the water. Rinse thoroughly in tap water and finally in distilled water. Dry in oven at 110°C-130°C.

3.1.2 *Preparation of sodium chloride solutions*

Dissolve 8.5 g of sodium chloride, A.C.S. or CP, in 1,000 ml of distilled water. Filter through hard paper and autoclave for 30 minutes at 121°C. Unless otherwise indicated this is the solution referred to in the text as salt solution. A solution of 8.5 g of sodium chloride in 100 ml of distilled water is required for the preparation of the haemoglobin solution used in making colour standards.

3.1.3 *Reagents for the haemolytic (indicator) system*

3.1.3.1 *Sheep erythrocytes.* Sheep blood may be collected and preserved in an equal volume of 2.5% sodium citrate solution. Preserved cells may be used for about one month. A pool of cells from more than one sheep may be used instead.

Filter blood through cotton into a graduated centrifuge-tube. Add 2 or 3 volumes of salt solution. Centrifuge at a speed sufficient to throw down cells. Remove the supernatant fluid, replace with fresh salt solution, mix, and centrifuge again. Repeat the process, but this time, centrifuge at a higher speed in order to pack the cells firmly. Wash cells until the supernatant fluid is shown to be free from serum albumin in a test with concentrated nitric acid (Heller's ring test). Three washings are usually sufficient. After the final washing, the supernatant fluid should be clear and colourless.

Read the volume of packed cells in the centrifuge-tube. Prepare a 5% suspension by adding sufficient salt solution to make the entire volume twenty times that of the packed cells. Shake the suspension thoroughly before withdrawing portions for use.

Check the accuracy of the 5% cell suspension by colorimetric or spectrophotometric analysis of an aliquot of the lysed cells. *Example :* To 0.4 ml of the 5% cell suspension add 7.1 ml of distilled water. Mix well to induce complete lysis of the sheep cells. In a Klett-Summerson instrument, with the green filter (No. 54), satisfactory readings are between 240 and 260. In a Coleman "junior" spectrophotometer, the 5% suspension diluted 1:15 in distilled water has an optical density about 6.0 at wave-length 545 mμ in 12 mm $\times$ 75 mm tubes.

3.1.3.2 *Antisheep amboceptor.* Rabbits are immunized by successive intravenous injections, during 4 weeks, of sheep serum and washed sheep-blood cells ; the schedule for immunization is given in table I.

TABLE I. SCHEDULE FOR IMMUNIZATION OF RABBITS *

Week	1		2			3		4		5
Day	Wed.	Fri.	Mon.	Wed.	Fri.	Wed.	Fri.	Mon.	Wed.	Mon.
Sheep serum (ml)	0.5	1.0	0.2	0.2	0.2		0.2	0.2	0.2	Bleed out from heart or carotid
			1.3**	1.8**	2.3**					
10% suspension of washed sheep-cells (ml).						1.0	2.0**	3.0**	4.0**	

* Modification of the method of Ulrich & McArthur [81]
**The interval between any two doses given on the same day to one rabbit should be thirty minutes.

All injections are given intravenously. The rabbits are bled on the first day of the 5th week. After animals are bled out, the blood is left overnight in the refrigerator ; serum is then removed from the clot, inactivated at 56°C for 30 minutes and preserved with an equal volume of CP glycerol. It is stored in a refrigerator.

3.1.3.3 *Complement.* Use the pooled serum of at least ten healthy guinea-pigs, males or non-pregnant females, bled after twelve hours of fasting. Collect blood from the heart or from the large blood vessels in the neck. In the latter case, stun the animal with a sharp blow on the head. Avoid cutting the oesophagus or trachea. Collect the blood from each into separate Petri dishes. Leave at room temperature for about 30 minutes ; rim the clots

TABLE II. TEST OF INDIVIDUAL GUINEA-PIG SERUM FOR HAEMOLYTIC ACTIVITY

Tube number	1	2
Guinea-pig serum (1 : 10 dilution)	0.04 ml	0.01 ml
Salt solution.	0.26 ml	0.29 ml
Sensitized sheep-cells	0.2 ml	0.2 ml
Incubate in a water-bath at 37ºC for 15 minutes		
Satisfactory degree of haemolysis	95% to 100%	5% to 70%

and set the dishes in a refrigerator for 30 minutes. Transfer the serum from each individual dish into a separate tube, and centrifuge. Remove each of the cell-free supernatant fluids to a second series of tubes. Keep in the refrigerator when not in use. Before pooling, test each serum for haemolytic activity, and for natural antisheep amboceptor ; the respective test-schemes are given in tables II and III.

TABLE III. TEST OF INDIVIDUAL GUINEA-PIG SERUM FOR NATURAL ANTISHEEP AMBOCEPTOR

Tube number	1
Guinea-pig serum (1 : 10 dilution)	0.1 ml
5% cell suspension	0.1 ml
Salt solution	0.3 ml
Incubate in a water-bath at 37ºC for 15 minutes	
Satisfactory degree of haemolysis.	5% or less

Complement preserved by rapid freezing or by evaporation in the frozen state in vacuo has proved satisfactory. Frozen complement should be thawed on the day of use. Lyophilized complement may be reconstituted with a preserving solution somewhat in advance of the day of testing. This solution is prepared by dissolving 20 g of boric acid and 100 g of sodium acetate ($NaC_2H_3O_2.3H_2O$) in distilled water to make 1,000 ml.

3.1.3.4 *Colour standards.* For reading tests and titrations, use colour standards representing different degrees of haemolysis ranging from 0% to 95% at intervals of 5%.

Into each of two graduated centrifuge-tubes, pipette 5 ml of the 5% sheep-cell suspension. To the first, add 5 ml of salt solution ; this gives 2.5% intact cells. Centrifuge the second tube at high speed and decant the supernatant, add distilled water to 9 ml, shake, and allow haemolysis to occur. Then add 1.0 ml of 8.5% salt solution ; this corresponds to a completely lysed 2.5% suspension of cells in isotonic saline. Guinea-pig serum diluted 1 : 30 is inactivated for 30 minutes in a water-bath at 56°C. Pipette the amounts indicated in table IV to make the colour standards.

The colour standard is intended to approximate the conditions of the test and should, therefore, be made of reagents actually in use. No account is taken of the antigen used in tests for syphilis nor of amboceptor, since they are essentially colourless. Several colour standards may be prepared by pipetting several times the above amounts into specimen-tubes, and dispensing 0.5 ml of each mixture into test-tubes.

To estimate haemolysis, all tubes of a test are first compared with the standards representing 70% haemolysis or more ; where no match is found, they are centrifuged and compared with the other standards (65% haemolysis or less).

The reaction may instead be read in a photo-electric colorimeter. For such reading the volume of the test must be adjusted by addition of an aliquot of cold salt solution before centrifuging and reading.

3.1.4 *Standardization of the haemolytic system*

3.1.4.1 *Amboceptor.* The dosage of amboceptor used is that optimally sensitizing for an equal volume of a 5% suspension of sheep cells ; i.e., it is

TABLE IV. COLOUR STANDARDS (AMOUNTS EXPRESSED IN ML)

Haemolysis %	95	90	85	80	75	70	65	60	55	50	45	40	35	30	25	20	15	10	5	0
2.5% haemolysed cells	.19	.18	.17	.16	.15	.14	.13	.12	.11	.10	.09	.08	.07	.06	.05	.04	.03	.02	.01	0.00
2.5% intact cells	.01	.02	.03	.04	.05	.06	.07	.08	.09	.10	.11	.12	.13	.14	.15	.16	.17	.18	.19	.20
Inactivated 1 : 30 complement	.3	.3	.3	.3	.3	.3	.3	.3	.3	.3	.3	.3	.3	.3	.3	.3	.3	.3	.3	.3
	Use these with cells in suspension						Centrifuge these													

TABLE V. ANTISHEEP AMBOCEPTOR TITRATION

Tube number	1	2	3	4	5	6	7	8
Complement 1:60 (ml)	0.1	0.1	0.1	0.1	0.1	0.1	—	—
Amboceptor 1:400 (ml)	0.3	0.2	0.1	0.05	0.03	0.02	0.4	—
Salt solution (ml) . .	—	0.1	0.2	0.25	0.27	0.28	—	0.4
5% suspension of sheep-cells (ml) . .	0.1	0.1	0.1	0.1	0.1	0.1	0.1	0.1
Incubate in a water-bath at 37ºC for 15 minutes								
Centrifuge and read percentage haemolysis by reference to colour standards								

the dose beyond which further increase of amboceptor gives no appreciable increase in the degree of partial haemolysis obtained with a given dose of complement. Under these conditions, the natural amboceptor contributed by the human serum to be tested has little effect.

The dilutions of amboceptor employed in titration are dependent upon the average potency of samples encountered in practice. Experience will dictate the appropriate range to be covered. The complement dose should be sufficient to produce about 50% haemolysis under the conditions of the test ; usually a 1 : 60 dilution is satisfactory. A titration should be made to determine the optimally sensitizing dose of each amboceptor for cells of each individual or combination of sheep whose cells are to be used. Make a 1 : 400 dilution of amboceptor in salt solution and titrate as indicated in table V.

TABLE VI. EXAMPLE TITRATION OF AMBOCEPTOR

Tube number	1	2	3	4	5	6	7 & 8
Equivalent dilution of amboceptor * . . .	1:133	1:200	1:400	1:800	1:1,330	1:2,000	controls **
Possible results of titration	50%	50%	50%	50%	40%	20%	no haemolysis

* Dilution required if the usual 0.1-ml amount were used.
** Control tubes 7 and 8 should show no haemolysis. If haemolysis occurs, the standardization is invalid.

An example is shown in table VI. The maximally sensitizing dose is that of the fourth tube. This amboceptor should be used in a dilution of 1: 800. The conclusion would be the same for any other resultant degree of haemolysis in tubes 1 to 4 inclusive—provided it were the same in all, greater than in tubes of higher number, and about 35% to 70%.

Once standardized, a single lot of glycerolated amboceptor retains its potency for long periods if kept at 3º-6ºC, and need be restandardized only once or twice a year.

To prepare sensitized cells for use, equal volumes of a 5% suspension of sheep cells and of the appropriate dilution of amboceptor, representing the optimally sensitizing dose, are mixed thoroughly and allowed to stand for ten minutes. Before pipetting any cells for use, the suspension should be mixed by mild agitation. Moreover, during incubation thereafter in tests, the cells should be kept in suspension by frequent gentle shaking.

TABLE VII. TITRATION OF COMPLEMENT

Tube number	1	2	3	4	5	6
Pooled guinea-pig serum 1 : 40 (ml)	0.09	0.08	0.07	0.06	0.05	0.04
Salt solution (ml)	0.21	0.22	0.23	0.24	0.25	0.26
Sensitized sheep-cells (ml) .	0.2	0.2	0.2	0.2	0.2	0.2
Incubate in a water-bath at 37ºC for 15 minutes						

TABLE VIII. FOR ESTIMATION OF DILUTION OF GUINEA-PIG SERUM CONTAINING 6 UNITS PER 0.1 ML

Tube number	1	2	3	4	5	6
If percentage haemolysis is	To 1 part of undiluted guinea-pig serum add the following parts of salt solution					
20	5.0	5.8	6.7	8.0	9.8	12.5
25	5.2	6.0	7.0	8.3	10.2	13.0
30	5.5	6.2	7.4	8.8	10.7	13.7
35	5.7	6.5	7.7	9.1	11.1	14.2
40	6.0	6.8	8.0	9.4	11.5	14.7
45	6.2	7.1	8.2	9.8	11.9	15.2
50	6.4	7.3	8.5	10.1	12.3	15.7
55	6.6	7.6	8.8	10.4	12.7	16.2
60	6.9	7.9	9.2	10.9	13.2	16.8
65	7.1	8.2	9.5	11.2	13.7	17.3
70	7.4	8.5	9.9	11.6	14.2	18.0
75	7.8	8.9	10.3	12.2	14.9	18.8
80	8.1	9.3	10.8	12.7	15.5	19.7

3.1.4.2 *Complement.* The unit of complement (the amount that is required for 50% haemolysis) is determined by titration, on the day the complement is to be used. Prepare two samples of 1:40 dilution of the pooled guinea-pig serum in salt solution. Titrate the haemolytic activity as indicated in table VII ; read by comparison with colour standards.

Use the average of the dilution figures indicated in table VIII for the separate tubes of the titration. The most desirable range is enclosed between the bold lines ; other properties of complement are less variable if we stay within these bounds. Prepare the complement dilution to contain 6 units in 0.1 ml. After ten minutes, prepare additional dilutions, as required, from that containing the six units per 0.1 ml. Check the accuracy as indicated in table IX ; satisfactory dilution will yield 70% to 85% haemolysis in each instance.

TABLE IX. CHECK ON ACCURACY OF COMPLEMENT DILUTIONS

Tube number	1	2	3	4
Dilution prepared to contain in 0.1 ml . .	6 units	3 units	2 units	1 unit
Amount of dilution tested (ml)	0.02	0.04	0.06	0.12
Salt solution (ml).	0.28	0.26	0.24	0.18
Sensitized sheep-cells (ml)	0.2	0.2	0.2	0.2
Incubate in a water-bath at 37ºC for 15 minutes				

3.1.5 *Preparation of the antigen*

To evaluate suitability for use in preparing antigens for the complement-fixation test for syphilis, a sample of cardiolipin or of lecithin is substituted in preparations otherwise made with materials previously found to be acceptable. The following formula is used invariably for the composition of the New York State Department of Health complement-fixation antigen :

	%
Cardiolipin	0.0175
Lecithin	0.0875
Cholesterol	0.3

An example of a card record of the preparation of antigen is given in table X.

Antigen. The antigen dosages indicated for use are those estimated as optimal for the given tests ; they are derived from the standardization procedures described by Maltaner & Maltaner. To dilute the antigen, place the required amount of salt solution in one beaker and pipette the antigen to the bottom of another ; then add salt solution to the

TABLE X. EXAMPLE OF PREPARATION CARD RECORD

Designation and lot number of test material :   Date :
To prepare 50-ml sample of cardiolipin-lecithin-cholesterol antigen

Cardiolipin :   0.0175% = 0.175 mg/ml = 8.75 mg/50 ml
Lecithin :   0.0875% = 0.875 mg/ml = 43.75 mg/50 ml
Cholesterol :   0.3   %

Cardiolipin :   designation and lot number (concentration in mg per ml)

$$\text{Amount (in ml) to use}* = \frac{8.75}{\text{concentration in mg per ml}} =$$

Lecithin :   designation and lot number (concentration in mg per ml)

$$\text{Amount (in ml) to use}* = \frac{43.75}{\text{concentration in mg per ml}} =$$

To the indicated amounts of cardiolipin and lecithin admix 25 ml of 0.6% cholesterol in dehydrated ethanol and make up to 50 ml in a volumetric flask with dehydrated ethanol.

* In preparing samples of cardiolipin-lecithin-cholesterol antigen, avoid pipetting less than 1 ml of cardiolipin or lecithin solution by using larger amounts in the same proportion if necessary.

antigen as rapidly as possible and mix thoroughly by pouring from one beaker to the other several times. Antigen dilutions are stable for several hours at room temperature, but should not be kept overnight.

3.1.6 *Preparation of serum*

Assign a serial number to each specimen, rim the clot, cap the tube, and centrifuge. Remove the serum from the clot, taking care not to transfer blood corpuscles. Sera showing marked haemolysis are likely to be unsatisfactory for serological tests.

On the morning of the day of the first examination, inactivate all sera for 30 minutes in a water-bath at 56°C. On each day of testing thereafter, inactivate sera at 56°C for five minutes. The bath temperature during inactivation must be maintained at 56°C ($\pm$0.2°). Sera stored in the refrigerator should be allowed to come to room temperature before being put in the water-bath. Cap all serum tubes before inactivation and during storage.

On any day it is to be used as diluent in the titration of reacting specimens, a sufficient quantity of pooled, non-reacting human serum, not more than seven days old, is heated for 30 minutes at 56°C. If required, prepare dilutions of patient's serum with such a pool and use 0.05 ml of the diluted or undiluted serum in each test.

All reagents prepared for the day's tests except the antigen must be kept refrigerated when not in use. Complement, alone, must be kept iced, even while in use. Reagents must be pipetted in the order indicated in the tables. The total volume in each reaction tube is 0.3 ml before addition of sheep cells, and 0.5 ml thereafter.

3.1.7 *Technical controls*

All reagents should be prepared carefully in accordance with the directions given. However, to guard against inadvertent errors in procedure, suitable simultaneous technical controls should be included for each batch of tests as indicated in tables XI and XII. In addition there should be some simultaneous tests of each kind made with serum specimens previously evaluated in the same way.

TABLE XI.   COMPLEMENT AND SENSITIZED-CELL-SUSPENSION CONTROLS

Tube number	Complement (in 0.1 ml)	Salt solution (ml)	Preliminary incubation	Sensitized cells (ml)	Period for haemolysis
1	1 unit	0.2	as prescribed for the test in question	0.2	as prescribed for the test in question
2	2 units	0.2		0.2	
3	none	0.3		0.2	

TABLE XII. ANTIGEN-DILUTION CONTROLS *

Tube number	Amount of antigen dilution (ml)	Complement (in 0.1 ml)	Salt solution (ml)	Preliminary incubation	Sensitized cells (ml)	Period for haemolysis
1	0.1	1 unit	0.1	as prescribed for the test in question	0.2	as prescribed for the test in question
2	0.1	2 units	0.1		0.2	

* Each dilution used should be so controlled.

3.1.8   Screening test

The one-tube screening test is performed as indicated in table XIII. All serum specimens are so tested with the reference-standard antigen (A_r).

TABLE XIII. SCREENING TEST

Patient's serum (undiluted)	0.05 ml
Antigen (dilution 1:133) *	0.1 ml
Complement (3 unit dilution)	0.1 ml
Salt solution	0.05 ml
Incubate at 3°-6°C for 2 hours, then in a water-bath at 37°C for 30 minutes	
Sensitized sheep-cells	0.2 ml
Incubate in a water-bath at 37°C for 15 minutes	

* The dose indicated is approximately the optimal dose under the conditions of the test.

Those that yield 95% to 100% haemolysis are called "non-reacting", and are used as needed for tests by the same technique on the following day with the antigen (A_t) in question. Of course, it is better, if practicable, to perform the A_t and A_r tests on the same day ; in any case safeguards, as mentioned above, should be provided by performing some tests simultaneously, as well as technical control tests to safeguard against use of unsatisfactory reagents.

3.1.9 "Low-titre" test

3.1.9.1 *Performance of the test.* If in the screening test with antigen A_t the reaction yields less than 95% haemolysis with a serum specimen, it is further investigated by use of a "low-titre" test made simultaneously with each antigen $(A_t$ and $A_r)$. These tests are made as indicated in table XIV.

TABLE XIV. "LOW-TITRE" TEST

Tube number		1	2	3	4
Patient's serum (undiluted) (ml)		0.05	0.05	0.05	0.05
Antigen	1:133 dilution * (ml) . .			0.1	
	1:67 dilution * (ml) . .				0.1
Complement	1 unit dilution (ml) . .	0.1			
	2 unit dilution (ml) . .		0.1		
	3 unit dilution (ml) . .			0.1	
	6 unit dilution (ml) . .				0.1
Salt solution (ml)		0.15	0.15	0.05	0.05
Incubate for 4 hours at 3°-6°C					
Sensitized sheep-cells (ml).		0.2	0.2	0.2	0.2
Incubate in a water-bath at 37°C for 15 minutes					

* The dose indicated is approximately the optimal dose under the given circumstances.

3.1.9.2 *Reading and expression of results.* Read haemolysis percentage by comparison with the colour standards. If the degrees of haemolysis obtained are within the range given in table XV, we may determine the

TABLE XV. EVALUATION OF THE INDEX TITRE (I) FROM PERCENTAGE HAEMOLYSIS OBTAINED IN THE "LOW-TITRE" TEST*

Tube number	Percentage haemolysis 5	10	15	20	25	30	35	40	45	50	55	60	65	70	75	80	85	90
1	1.78	1.54	1.39	1.32	1.23	1.19	1.12	1.09	1.04	1.00	**	**	**	**	**	**	**	**
2	3.51	3.06	2.81	2.63	2.49	2.37	2.26	2.16	2.07	2.00	1.92	1.84	1.76	1.69	1.60	1.52	1.42	1.29
3	5.02	4.45	4.12	3.88	3.69	3.52	3.37	3.24	3.10	3.00	2.86	2.75	2.64	2.52	2.40	2.26	2.12	1.92
4	9.05	8.25	7.75	7.40	7.20	6.80	6.65	6.35	6.20	6.00	5.76	5.59	5.39	5.16	4.93	4.65	4.37	3.98

* The estimated amount of complement (K') required for 50 % haemolysis is given in accord with the actual percentage haemolysis obtained in each tube. The index titre (I) is the maximum value of K' for tubes 3 and 4 divided by the maximum K' for tubes 1 and 2.

K'_S is the maximum value obtained with tubes 1 and 2.

$K'_{S,A}$ is the maximum value obtained with tubes 3 and 4.

$I = K'_{S,A}/K'_S$; $I_t = I$ with antigen A_t ; $I_r = I$ with antigen A_r.

** For tube 1 take the value for 50 % haemolysis if the actual haemolysis is greater.

index titre $I = K'_{S,A}/K'_S$ where K'_S is the maximum value for tubes 1 and 2, and $K'_{S,A}$ is the maximum value for tubes 3 and 4. This notation is in accord with the proposal for uniformity by Thompson et al. [80] Accordingly, x' denotes the total amount of complement introduced originally ; and K' is the value of x' estimated as required to produce 50% haemolysis under the given conditions. These conditions are briefly indicated by use of subscripts ; thus, K'_S is the value for 0.05 ml of patient's serum without antigen, and $K'_{S,A}$ is the corresponding value with antigen. To avoid the division, the value for I may be obtained directly from tables XVI and XVII. Care must be taken to choose between the data of tubes 3 and 4, as between the data of tubes 1 and 2, so as to use maximum values of $K'_{S,A}$ as well as maximum K'_S.

For convenience we let I_r denote the value of I obtained with the reference-standard antigen (A_r) and let I_t denote that obtained with the test-antigen (A_t) made simultaneously on the same specimen.

3.1.9.3 *Definition of " defective" observation and sequential test for excessive reactivity.* The universe sampled consists of observations made as prescribed with antigens A_r and A_t upon specimens "non-reacting" in the screening test with antigen A_r (i.e., yielding 95% haemolysis or more), but exclusive of any observation that cannot be classified unequivocally as either defective or non-defective as follows :

(1) If, in the screening test, A_t yields 95% haemolysis or more, the observation is called non-defective, and no further tests are made on the specimen. Otherwise, a " low-titre " test is made simultaneously with A_r and A_t.

(2) If this " low-titre " test is made, the observation is called : defective if $I_t \geq 2$ and also $2\ (I_t - I_r)/(I_t + I_r) > 0.16$; non-defective if either $I_t < 2$ or $2\ (I_t - I_r)/(I_t + I_r) \leq 0.16$.

(3) If the " low-titre " test does not yield actual values of I_t and I_r needed for decision under (2) above, there may still be a clear indication of greater differences of the kinds specified so that obvious extension of (2) permits classification as defective or non-defective.

If decision cannot be made, the observation is called inadmissible and is rejected ; but an attempt is first made to avoid such rejection by repeating the test one or more times.

The purpose here is to provide a safeguard against excessive reactivity, especially if non-specific. Suppose that we have n admissible observations and that a of those are defective. We let ϕ denote the unknown relative frequency of non-defective observations in the sampled universe U ; and suppose that we are willing to accept the antigen-component lot in question if there is not more than a 2 % risk that ϕ is less than 0.975 ; and that we are willing to reject the lot if there is not more than a 2% risk that ϕ is greater than 0.995 ; otherwise, we will take another observation. The table for

TABLE XVI. ESTIMATE OF THE INDEX TITRE (*I*) USING THE DATA OF TUBE 3 IN THE "LOW-TITRE" TEST

	Percentage haemolysis in tube 3																	
Percentage haemolysis in tube 1 or 2 **	5	10	15	20	25	30	35	40	45	50	55	60	65	70	75	80	85	90
5	2.79	2.47	2.28	2.15	2.06	1.96	1.87	1.80	1.73	1.66	1.60	1.53	1.47	1.41	1.34	1.26	1.17	1.07
10	3.24	2.88	2.65	2.49	2.37	2.27	2.18	2.07	2.00	1.92	1.85	1.77	1.71	1.63	1.55	1.46	1.36	1.24
15	3.56	3.15	2.92	2.74	2.63	2.49	2.39	2.29	2.20	2.11	2.03	1.95	1.87	1.79	1.70	1.60	1.50	1.36
20	3.80	3.38	3.13	2.94	2.80	2.67	2.55	2.45	2.35	2.26	2.17	2.08	2.00	1.91	1.82	1.72	1.60	1.46
25	4.03	3.59	3.31	3.12	2.97	2.83	2.72	2.60	2.49	2.40	2.30	2.21	2.12	2.03	1.92	1.83	1.70	1.55
30	4.25	3.76	3.49	3.27	3.13	2.98	2.85	2.74	2.63	2.52	2.43	2.33	2.24	2.14	2.03	1.92	1.79	1.63
35	4.44	3.95	3.64	3.42	3.26	3.13	2.99	2.86	2.75	2.64	2.54	2.44	2.33	2.24	2.12	2.00	1.86	1.70
40	4.63	4.11	3.78	3.57	3.40	3.25	3.12	2.99	2.86	2.75	2.65	2.54	2.43	2.32	2.22	2.09	1.94	1.77
45	4.82	4.28	3.94	3.72	3.55	3.39	3.24	3.10	2.99	2.86	2.75	2.65	2.53	2.42	2.30	2.18	2.03	1.85
50 *	5.02	4.45	4.12	3.88	3.69	3.52	3.37	3.24	3.10	3.00	2.86	2.75	2.64	2.52	2.40	2.26	2.12	1.92
55 *	5.24	4.62	4.29	4.04	3.84	3.67	3.52	3.37	3.24	3.12	2.99	2.86	2.75	2.63	2.50	2.36	2.20	2.00
60 *	5.44	4.83	4.45	4.19	4.00	3.81	3.65	3.50	3.36	3.23	3.11	2.99	2.86	2.73	2.60	2.45	2.28	2.08
65 *	5.67	5.04	4.64	4.40	4.18	3.98	3.82	3.65	3.52	3.38	3.24	3.12	2.99	2.85	2.71	2.56	2.40	2.18
70 *	5.94	5.30	4.87	4.58	4.38	4.19	4.00	3.83	3.68	3.53	3.40	3.26	3.13	2.98	2.84	2.69	2.50	2.27
75 *	6.25	5.55	5.13	4.83	4.59	4.40	4.20	4.03	3.88	3.72	3.57	3.43	3.30	3.14	2.98	2.82	2.63	2.40
80 *	6.65	5.87	5.44	5.12	4.86	4.64	4.45	4.27	4.10	3.94	3.79	3.64	3.48	3.33	3.15	2.98	2.79	2.54
85 *	7.15	6.30	5.82	5.48	5.23	4.97	4.76	4.56	4.40	4.21	4.05	3.89	3.74	3.57	3.39	3.20	2.98	2.72
90 *	7.75	6.90	6.35	6.00	5.71	5.46	5.23	5.00	4.81	4.62	4.44	4.25	4.09	3.90	3.72	3.51	3.27	2.97

* If tube 1 is used, take the values for 50 % haemolysis if the actual haemolysis is greater.

** Use data of either tube 1 or 2, whichever gives the maximum value for K'_S. If tube 1 is used, an estimate of I is as tabulated ; if tube 2 is used, half the tabular value is taken instead.

TABLE XVII. ESTIMATE OF THE INDEX TITRE (I) USING THE DATA OF TUBE 4 IN THE "LOW-TITRE" TEST

Percentage haemolysis in tube 4

Tube 1 or 2**	90	85	80	75	70	65	60	55	50	45	40	35	30	25	20	15	10	5
5	2.22	2.43	2.60	2.74	2.88	3.00	3.11	3.23	3.34	3.44	3.55	3.69	3.82	3.97	4.13	4.32	4.58	4.97
10	2.56	2.82	3.02	3.18	3.34	3.47	3.60	3.73	3.85	3.98	4.12	4.27	4.43	4.58	4.78	5.00	5.35	5.83
15	2.81	3.10	3.31	3.50	3.66	3.80	3.95	4.10	4.23	4.37	4.52	4.69	4.85	5.05	5.25	5.52	5.84	6.40
20	3.02	3.31	3.54	3.74	3.92	4.07	4.23	4.38	4.53	4.67	4.84	5.01	5.20	5.43	5.63	5.88	6.25	6.80
25	3.20	3.50	3.75	3.95	4.14	4.32	4.49	4.63	4.80	4.95	5.13	5.33	5.52	5.73	5.95	6.25	6.65	7.25
30	3.36	3.70	3.95	4.17	4.38	4.55	4.71	4.88	5.05	5.23	5.40	5.60	5.79	6.05	6.25	6.60	7.00	7.70
35	3.52	3.85	4.13	4.36	4.56	4.75	4.94	5.13	5.32	5.49	5.65	5.85	6.10	6.30	6.55	6.85	7.30	8.00
40	3.67	4.02	4.30	4.54	4.76	4.96	5.15	5.34	5.52	5.68	5.89	6.15	6.30	6.60	6.80	7.20	7.65	8.30
45	3.82	4.19	4.48	4.73	4.95	5.17	5.38	5.56	5.74	5.92	6.15	6.30	6.60	6.80	7.15	7.45	7.90	8.70
50*	3.98	4.37	4.65	4.93	5.16	5.39	5.59	5.76	6.00	6.20	6.35	6.65	6.80	7.20	7.40	7.75	8.25	9.05
55*	4.13	4.54	4.85	5.14	5.40	5.62	5.81	6.05	6.25	6.40	6.70	6.90	7.20	7.45	7.75	8.10	8.60	9.40
60*	4.30	4.71	5.05	5.35	5.60	5.81	6.10	6.25	6.50	6.70	6.90	7.20	7.45	7.75	8.05	8.40	8.95	9.80
65*	4.50	4.93	5.29	5.59	5.84	6.15	6.30	6.60	6.75	7.00	7.25	7.50	7.75	8.10	8.35	8.75	9.35	10.3
70*	4.70	5.16	5.54	5.83	6.15	6.35	6.65	6.80	7.10	7.30	7.60	7.80	8.20	8.45	8.80	9.20	9.75	10.7
75*	4.95	5.44	5.80	6.15	6.40	6.75	6.95	7.20	7.45	7.70	7.90	8.20	8.55	8.85	9.25	9.70	10.3	11.3
80*	5.25	5.74	6.20	6.50	6.80	7.15	7.40	7.70	7.85	8.20	8.45	8.75	9.10	9.40	9.80	10.3	10.9	11.9
85*	5.62	6.20	6.60	6.95	7.30	7.65	7.85	8.20	8.50	8.75	9.05	9.35	9.70	10.2	10.5	11.0	11.7	12.7
90*	6.20	6.75	7.25	7.70	8.00	8.30	8.65	8.95	9.25	9.60	9.90	10.3	10.7	11.1	11.5	12.0	12.8	14.0

(left margin label: Percentage haemolysis in tube 1 or 2**)

* If tube 1 is used, take the values for 50 % haemolysis, if the actual haemolysis is greater.

** Use data of either tube 1 or 2, whichever gives the maximum value for K'_S. If tube 1 is used, an estimate of I is as tabulated; if tube 2 is used, half the tabular value is taken instead.

direct-probability sequential decisions for $\alpha = \beta = 0.02$, $p' = 0.975$, and $p'' = 0.995$ indicates the earliest opportunity at which these decisions can be made (see table XX). However, to guard against the influence of correlation between observations made on the same day with the same reagent, we agree that not more than 40% of the total number of observations (n) shall be made on any given day.

It should be noted that in such tests, rejection is final, but acceptance only tentative pending like acceptance in the other prescribed tests. In our experience with many different test-antigens the test given above rarely led to a defective observation in the first 155, and all were accepted in this respect.

3.1.10 " High-titre " test

3.1.10.1 *Performance of the test.* Sera that yield 15% haemolysis or less in the screening test are submitted to a " high-titre " test ; where a sufficient volume (2 ml or more) remains, these sera may be used in parallel tests with A_t and A_r antigens. The technique involves use of successive dilutions of the given serum with diluent serum ; the dilution factors $D = 1$, 1.3, 1.8, 2.4, 3.2, 4.2, 5.6, 7.5, 10, 13, 18, and 24.

D	Patient's serum (ml)	Diluent serum (ml)
1.0	0.05	0.00
1.3	0.20	0.06
1.8	0.15	0.12
2.4	0.10	0.14
3.2	0.08	0.176
4.2	0.07	0.224
5.6	0.05	0.23
7.5	0.04	0.26
10	0.03	0.27
13	0.02	0.24
18	0.02	0.34
24	0.02	0.46

These dilutions are pipetted in 0.05 ml amounts, respectively, in successive tubes numbered 1 to 12. Then, to each are added : the optimal dose of antigen (0.1 ml of a 1 : 67 dilution), 0.1 ml of complement (6 unit dilution), and 0.05 ml of salt solution. The tubes are incubated for four hours at 3°–6°C. Then, 0.2 ml of sensitized sheep cells are added to each, and the tubes are incubated for fifteen minutes in a water-bath at 37°C.

3.1.10.2 *Reading.* Each tube is read by comparison with the colour standards, and $D(K'_{\mathrm{s,A}} - 1)$ is found by reference to table XVIII wherever

TABLE XVIII. VALUES OF $D(K'_{S,A} - 1)$ FROM "HIGH-TITRE" TESTS WITH 6 UNITS OF COMPLEMENT *

Per-centage haemo-lysis	D (dilution factor)							
	1	1.3	1.8	2.4	3.2	4.2	5.6	7.5
5	8.05	10.5	14.5	19.3	25.8	33.8	45.1	60.4
10	7.25	9.43	13.1	17.4	23.2	30.5	40.6	54.4
15	6.75	8.78	12.2	16.2	21.6	28.4	37.8	50.6
20	6.40	8.32	11.5	15.4	20.5	26.9	35.8	48.0
25	6.20	8.06	11.2	14.9	19.8	26.0	34.7	46.5
30	5.80	7.54	10.4	13.9	18.6	24.4	32.5	43.5
35	5.65	7.35	10.2	13.6	18.1	23.7	31.6	42.4
40	5.35	6.96	9.63	12.8	17.1	22.5	30.0	40.1
45	5.20	6.76	9.36	12.5	16.6	21.8	29.1	39.0
50	5.00	6.50	9.00	12.0	16.0	21.0	28.0	37.5
55	4.76	6.19	8.57	11.4	15.2	20.0	26.7	35.7
60	4.59	5.97	8.26	11.0	14.7	19.3	25.7	34.4
65	4.39	5.71	7.90	10.5	14.0	18.4	24.6	32.9
70	4.16	5.41	7.49	9.98	13.3	17.5	23.3	31.2
75	3.93	5.11	7.07	9.43	12.6	16.5	22.0	29.5
80	3.65	4.75	6.57	8.76	11.7	15.3	20.4	27.4
85	3.37	4.38	6.07	8.09	10.8	14.2	18.9	25.3
90	2.98	3.87	5.36	7.15	9.54	12.5	16.7	22.4

* In the test, 6 units of complement with a volume of patient's serum equal to (0.05 ml)/D gave an observed degree of haemolysis ; $K'_{S,A}$ is the estimated amount of complement required for 50% haemolysis. Under these conditions, one unit of complement must be free and therefore approximately $K'_{S,A} - 1$ units are fixed. Thus, the amount of fixation per 0.05 ml of patient's serum is $D(K'_{S,A} - 1)$ as given in the table.

the percentage haemolysis is within the tabulated range. We take the greatest value of $D(K'_{S,A} - 1)$ in the set for a given serum and antigen preparation provided it is not less than 4 and either $D = 1$ or else there is one other value not less than 7/9 of the greatest value of $D(K'_{S,A} - 1)$. Table XIX gives an example of such an evaluation ; in this case 23.7 as obtained for tube 6 is taken.

The high-titre test as given in the text is not used in routine work, though it could be. Since the values of $D(K'_{S,A} - 1)$ are obtained simultaneously with the antigens A_t and A_r (used in parallel tests), the serum-control value (K'_S) would be obtained from the same tube, since no antigen is used in this. The question of what is the best titre to use is still open ; the principal issues have been set forth by Thompson et al. [80] It should be

**TABLE XIX. EXAMPLE OF EVALUATION OF
A " HIGH-TITRE " TEST**

Tube number	D	Percentage haemolysis	$D(K'_{S,A} - 1)$
3	1.8	0	—
4	2.4	0	—
5	3.2	20	20.5
6	4.2	35	23.7
7	5.6	90	16.7
8	7.5	100	—

noted that under conditions yielding 50% haemolysis, the amount of complement present is always one unit more than the amount fixed. At the time the index-titre, $I = K'_{S,A}/K'_S$, was proposed for use it seemed simpler to use than $I - 1$; but the latter would have had the advantage of being zero rather than 1 where there is no specific reaction. However, many of the possible considerations in determining titres for serodiagnosis are relatively of minor importance in comparing reactions with two different antigen preparations and the same serum.

3.1.10.3 *Definition of " defective " observation and sequential test for approximate equivalence of reaction.* The universe sampled consists of observations made as prescribed with antigens A_r and A_t upon " reacting " specimens, those that give 15% haemolysis or less in the screening test with A_r and that have 2 ml or more of the specimen remaining for this purpose, provided that the observation in each case to be admissible can be classified unequivocally as either defective or non-defective as defined below.

Simultaneous " high-titre " tests are made on a given specimen with each antigen ; the resulting maximal value for $D(K'_{S,A} - 1)$ with A_r is denoted by T_r, that with A_t is denoted by T_t. The relative discrepancy R is defined as $\pm 2(T_t - T_r)/(T_t + T_r)$ whichever is not negative. For the present purpose, an observation is called : defective if $R > 0.16$; non-defective if $R \leq 0.16$; and inadmissible if no such decision is given by the data.

The purpose here is to provide a test of approximate equivalence of reactivity in " high-titre " tests. Again, we suppose that we have n admissible observations and that a of these are defective. We let ϕ denote the unknown relative frequency of non-defective observations in the sampled universe U; and suppose that : we are willing to accept the antigen-component lot in this respect if there is not more than a 2% risk that $\phi < 0.75$; to reject it if there is not more than a 2% risk that $\phi > 0.85$; and, otherwise, to take another observation.   The table for direct-probability sequential decisions for $a = \beta = 0.02$, $p' = 0.75$, and $p'' = 0.85$ indicates the earliest opportunity at which these decisions can be made (see table XX)

TABLE XX.   DIRECT-PROBABILITY SEQUENTIAL DECISIONS INDICATING THE EARLIEST OPPORTUNITY FOR ACCEPTANCE OR REJECTION *

									$a = \beta = 0.02$ $p' = 0.975$ $p'' = 0.995$		
			$a = \beta = 0.02$, $p' = 0.75$, $p'' = 0.85$								
a	n'_a	n''_a	a	n'_a	n''_a	a	n'_a	n''_a	a	n'_a	n''_a
0	14	—	20	120	83	40	213	193	0	155	—
1	21	—	21	125	88	41	218	198	1	231	4
2	28	—	22	130	93	42	222	204	2	299	43
3	34	4	23	134	99	43	227	210	3	362	114
4	39	7	24	139	104	44	231	215	4	421	204
5	45	11	25	144	109	45	236	221	5	479	307
6	50	15	26	149	115	46	240	227	6	536	419
7	56	19	27	153	120	47	245	233	7	—	538
8	61	24	28	158	126	48	249	238			
9	66	28	29	163	131	49	254	244			
10	71	33	30	167	137	50	258	250			
11	76	37	31	172	142	51	263	256			
12	81	42	32	177	148	52	267	261			
13	86	47	33	181	153	53	—	267			
14	91	52	34	186	159						
15	96	57	35	190	164						
16	101	62	36	195	170						
17	106	67	37	200	176						
18	111	72	38	204	181						
19	115	77	39	209	187						

* With a stipulated (a, β, p', p'') in use of a direct-probability sequential system, after n observations we note the number, a, that are defective in the given sense, and then : we accept the lot if n is not less than n'_a ; we reject it if n is not more than n''_a ; or, otherwise, we take another observation.

provided that the observations may be considered independent.   However, several observations are made simultaneously with the same reagent preparations (complement, sensitized sheep cells, etc.).   To guard against this possible introduction of a correlation between observations made on the same day, it was further agreed never to make a decision unless we have the equivalent of at least 20 observations with not more than 40% of the total observations made on any one day. Actually fewer observations obviously give the equivalent of this in some cases.

TABLE XXI. EXAMPLE OF APPLICATION OF DIRECT-PROBABILITY SEQUENTIAL ANALYSIS TO THE " HIGH-TITRE " TEST *

$\alpha = \beta = 0.02, \; p' = 0.75, \; p'' = 0.85$											
n	T_r	T_t	a	n	T_r	T_t	a	n	T_r	T_t	a
(first day's results)				(second day's results)				(third day's results)			
1	22.5	22.5	0	13	19.3	19.3	3	22	25.8	25.8	3
2	73.5	67.5	0	14	30.5	30.5	3	23	7.90	7.07	3
3	26.9	28.4	0	15	8.32	8.32	3	24	26.0	26.0	3
4	19.3	19.3	0	16	26.0	26.0	3	25	33.8	33.8	3
5	12.0	11.2	0	17	16.0	16.0	3	26	17.4	15.4	3
6	35.8	35.8	0	18	17.4	15.4	3	27	67.6	67.5	3
7	17.1	13.1	1†	19	17.1	16.6	3	28	15.2	14.7	3
8	12.0	9.36	2†	20	19.8	19.8	3	29	23.7	24.4	3
9	154	139	2	21	14.9	13.6	3	30	12.5	12.5	3
10	59.7	46.5	3†					31	4.16	4.16	3
11	13.6	13.1	3					32	12.5	12.0	3
12	37.5	37.5	3					33	13.6	13.9	3
								34††	30.5	30.5	3

* Defective observation is defined as one for which the relative discrepancy exceeds 16%.
† An increase of one in a occurs whenever a defective observation is encountered.
†† By reference to table XX, we reach a decision for $n = 34$ with $a = 3$; accordingly we accept.

As mentioned in section 3.1.9.3, rejection is final, but acceptance only tentative pending results from the other prescribed tests. An example of the application of the " high-titre " sequential test is given in table XXI.

3.2 New York State Department of Health Microscopic Slide Test for Acceptance of New Lots of Antigen Components

3.2.1 *Equipment, glassware, and reagents*

General equipment

1. Electric rotating-machine with automatic-timing device, single speed, automatic timer up to five minutes, or machine with variable speeds, automatic timer up to thirty minutes
2. Ringmaker—metal, hand-operated or automatic, to make 1.5-cm paraffin rings
3. Hypodermic needles—26-gauge, 3/8 inch regular bevel, or 23-gauge, 3/4 inch regular bevel
4. Microscope—monocular, fitted with 16-mm objective and 10 × ocular

Glassware

1. Pipettes : 10.0 ml graduated in 0.1 ml
   5.0 ml graduated in 0.1 ml
   1.0 ml graduated in 0.01 ml
   0.2 ml graduated in 0.01 ml or
   0.1 ml graduated in 0.05 ml
   2.5 ml volumetric pipette standardized to deliver the required volume in 30 to 35 seconds
2. Test-tubes : 100 mm × 15 mm
3. Slides : 3 inches × 2 inches (75 mm × 50 mm)
4. Syringe : 1-ml glass-tip tuberculin-type syringe
5. Bottles : 100-ml Pyrex glass bottles with standard tapered stoppers
   30-ml Pyrex glass bottles fitted with screw caps lined with aluminium foil

Reagents

1. Salt solution : physiological salt solution (0.85% NaCl)
2. Cardiolipin or lecithin : reference standards
3. Dehydrated, redistilled ethanol
4. Pure cholesterol

3.2.2 *Preparation of the antigen*

Prepare a solution in dehydrated ethanol containing 0.03% cardiolipin, 0.3% lecithin, and 0.9% cholesterol. The amount of the solution prepared should be such that the amounts of cardiolipin and lecithin solutions to be measured are not less than 0.5 ml.

Two antigens are prepared : one, composed of reagents known to be satisfactory and which serves as a standard antigen and the other, the test antigen, made with standard reagents with the exception of the cardiolipin or lecithin under inspection. Volumes are calculated to the nearest 0.01 ml.

Weigh accurately the desired amount of cholesterol and transfer to a bottle. The reagents are pipetted in the following order : cardiolipin, lecithin, and dehydrated ethanol. Small volumes should be carefully pipetted to the bottom of the bottle. Use pipettes in sequence to give maximal accuracy. For example, use 10-ml pipettes to deliver full 10-ml volumes, 5-ml pipettes to deliver volumes between 10 ml and 1 ml, and 1-ml pipettes for volumes less than 1 ml. Mix reagents thoroughly and allow to stand at room temperature until the cholesterol is completely dissolved. The antigen should be water-clear, and free from colour and particulate material. Antigens are stored in a dark cabinet at room temperature.

3.2.3 *Preparation of slides and serum*

Paraffin-ringed slides. All glassware must be chemically clean. Serum will spread within the circles on clean slides. Failure to spread indicates that the slide is not clean and should not be used. Place twelve rings of melted paraffin (1.5-cm diameter) on each slide, using either a hand-operated or an automatic ringmaker.

Blood serum. Centrifuge whole clotted blood at 2,500 r.p.m. for eight minutes. Transfer the clear serum to a clean tube. Heat in a water-bath at 56°C for 30 minutes on the day it is to be tested, and cool to room temperature before testing. All sera should be free of precipitate. Examine when removed from the water-bath, and recentrifuge those that are not cleared.

3.2.4 *Suspension of antigen*

Preparation. Pipette 0.5 ml of antigen into the bottom of a tube (100 mm by 15 mm). While shaking the tube gently, allow 2.5 ml of 0.85 % salt solution to run down the side of the tube from a pipette standardized to deliver 2.5 ml in 30-35 seconds. After the salt solution is delivered, mix by shaking thoroughly. Centrifuge at approximately 2,500 r.p.m. for ten minutes, decant the supernatant fluid rapidly and thoroughly, and resuspend the sediment in 1.5 ml of salt solution.

Dispensing. Dispense the antigen suspension from either a 26-gauge or a 23-gauge hypodermic needle attached to a 1-ml tuberculin-type syringe held in a vertical position. The needles should be selected so that the 26-gauge needle delivers approximately 200 drops of antigen suspension per ml (0.005 ml per drop) and the 23-gauge needle, approximately 100 drops per ml (0.01 ml per drop). Needles should be checked daily before use. This method of delivering antigen has been found to be practical and its

FIG. 1. DEGREES OF FLOCCULATION IN MICROSCOPIC SLIDE TEST

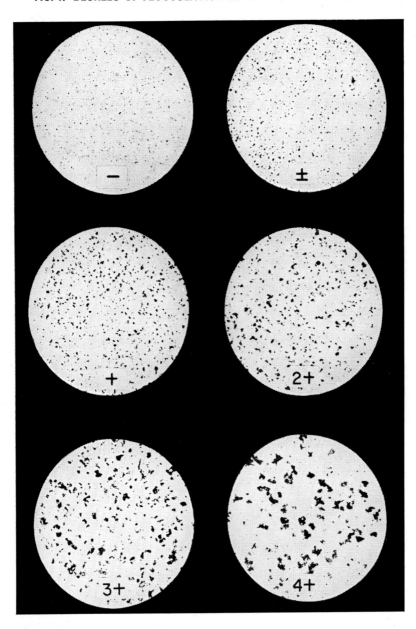

— Particles evenly dispersed

± Particles irregularly distributed

+ Small clumps, evenly distributed

2+ Larger clumps, with clearing of suspension

3+ Progressively larger clumps, macro-scopically visible

4+ Larger clumps, macroscopically visible, suspension clear

use is recommended. If other methods are employed, care must be taken to ensure that the correct amount of suspension is delivered.

Preliminary tests. Before use, make control tests of the antigen suspension with 0.85% salt solution, with an undiluted non-reacting serum, and with an undiluted strongly reacting serum. Perform the tests in the manner described in section 3.2.5.

The antigen suspension should be evenly dispersed in the salt solution and in the non-reacting serum ; in the reacting serum, there should be marked clumping. Do not use an antigen suspension that is not satisfactory in these controls. The suspension is satisfactory for an 8-hour period when kept at room temperature.

3.2.5 *Performance and reading of the test*

Pipette 0.05 ml of serum in a single ring and spread it over the surface. Do not pipette more than forty sera at one time since evaporation occurs and the reactions are not stable. Resuspend the antigen emulsion by shaking, draw the suspension into the 1-ml syringe, and remove the plunger. Holding the syringe, with 26-gauge needle attached, in a vertical position, allow one drop of antigen (0.005 ml) to fall on to each serum. Shake the slides on a rotator for four minutes at 180 r.p.m.

Reading. Examine at once with a microscope of 16-mm objective and $10 \times$ magnification. Record as $-$, $\pm$, $+$, $2+$, $3+$, or $4+$, according to the degree of clumping and clearing :

- $-$ particles evenly dispersed ; no clumping
- $\pm$ particles irregularly distributed ; a few tiny aggregates
- $+$ small clumps, evenly distributed
- $2+$ larger clumps, with clearing of suspension
- $3+$ progressively larger clumps, macroscopically visible
- $4+$ progressively larger clumps, macroscopically visible, suspension clear

Photographs typical of the various degrees of reaction have been prepared for initial use as aids in reading (see fig. 1).

Immediately after reading, add a second drop of antigen suspension (0.005 ml) to each of the sera, rotate the slides, and read and record as before. It is important that the tests be read as quickly as possible after rotation and in any case within 3 minutes, since the reactions are not stable and will become progressively stronger if the test is permitted to stand.

Prozone reaction. Occasionally, a strongly reacting serum exhibits a prozone reaction when tested undiluted. Such a reaction may be characterized by the appearance of a few feathery clumps of varying size with a background of unprecipitated particles, or merely as a weak reaction. In such instances, more than two drops of antigen may be required to demonstrate maximum flocculation.

Test with diluted serum. Dilute the serum in physiological salt solution, preparing each dilution from the original serum. Use not less than 0.02 ml of serum for each dilution. Test a series of dilutions of the serum, such as : 1:2.5, 1:5, 1:10, 1:15, 1:20, 1:30, 1:40, 1:50, 1:60, 1:70, 1:80, 1:90, 1:100, 1:125, etc. Perform the test with diluted serum in the same manner as with undiluted serum but use only one drop of antigen (0.005 ml). The titre is defined as the highest dilution to give a 2+ degree of precipitation.

3.2.6 Comparative examination of sera with test and standard antigens

On each of three days the following sera are tested in parallel with a test antigen and a standard antigen :

(1) ten non-reacting, presumably non-syphilitic, sera ;
(2) ten syphilitic sera of low titre ;
(3) ten syphilitic sera of moderate or strong titre ;
(4) one strongly reacting pool, tested in dilution.

With the exception of the reacting pool, no serum is used more than once in the evaluation of any one test antigen.

3.2.7 Evaluation of results given by comparative testing

The criteria for accepting a reagent as satisfactory for use in the New York State Department of Health microscopic slide test are empirical ; no statistical method of evaluation has as yet been evolved for this test. However, if the rules enumerated below are followed, reasonably consistent results can be expected.

(1) Test-antigen suspensions in saline and non-reacting serum controls must be evenly dispersed and of the same size as those of the standard antigen. Aggregates obtained with reacting serum and test antigen should exhibit the same physical appearance, with respect to size and compactness, as those given with the standard.

(2) No reactions should be obtained with non-syphilitic sera and test antigen.

(3) Differences in degrees of reactions will occur with syphilitic sera. Minor differences attributable to limitations inherent in the test are not considered significant. By a significant difference is meant a variation of at least one degree of reaction, appearing with both doses of antigen suspension, between the results given with a test antigen and a standard antigen with the same serum. An example is given below :

Readings with antigen A		Readings with antigen B		Significant difference
1st drop	2nd drop	1st drop	2nd drop	
2+	3+	2+	2+	no
2+	3+	3+	3+	no
2+	3+	3+	4+	yes
2+	3+	1+	2+	yes

It has been found that in comparing satisfactory antigens one can expect to find significant differences, as defined above, in at least 10% of the reacting sera tested, but such differences should not be found in more than 25% of the reacting sera. In general, these differences should not be greater in degree than those given in the example above. If the test antigen gives results consistently stronger or weaker than the standard, a difference in sensitivity is indicated and therefore the test sample is unsatisfactory.

(4) No evidence of prozone phenomena should appear with the test antigen unless also present in tests with standard antigen.

(5) Titres obtained with the two antigens and diluted reacting sera should agree exactly in 50%—60% of the tests made. Such differences as do occur should not be greater than that reflected by one serum dilution. For example :

Titre with antigen A	Titre with antigen B	Significant difference
30	40	no
30	20	no
30	15	yes
30	50	yes

ANNEX 1

DIRECT-PROBABILITY SEQUENTIAL ANALYSIS

Introduction to Applications

Thompson broached the subjects of sequential analysis and of objective (cybernetic) experiment-steering systems in two articles, [70, 71] and gave fundamental relations in a third [72] that require only appropriate interpretation to allow development of the direct-probability sequential analysis systems that have been described in several brief notes. [48, 73, 74, 77, 79] Systematic methods have been given for stepwise extension of existing tables, as required. [63, 70, 75, 76] An experiment-steering system using direct-probability sequential analysis has been described in detail elsewhere.[78]

After stipulation of the conditions under which we are to accept or reject a lot, sequential analysis may be used to indicate that we have obtained enough data to permit such a decision one way or the other ; the most efficient system, of course, will indicate such a decision at the earliest opportunity. It should be obvious that such a sequential system is not designed to provide a justification of the stipulated conditions upon which it is based ; its purpose is simply to indicate when we have enough data to permit a decision on the stipulated basis.

In choosing the basis for decisions our judgement should be influenced by several things including : (1) availability of statistical methods and tables for the sequential analysis ; and (2) availability of materials, equipment, trained personnel, and time to implement the application. Thus a choice of the basis for decisions must be a compromise between desired satisfaction in the decisions and difficulties faced in obtaining requisite data. Thus, improvement of methods of preparation of materials to be tested or the means of testing them might afford greater satisfaction in our decisions or better economy in attaining them, possibly by a change in the stipulations. On the other hand, less skilled observations or an insidious modification of technique might impair our satisfaction or leave us with a false sense of security. The mathematician's service in this is to convert the stipulated conditions without alteration to a form permitting readier appreciation of some of their features, or to a form more convenient in application. It may become apparent that some features of certain stipulations (in use or under consideration) are inadequate or even opposed to our purpose. Perhaps economy can be served by a change.

Part of the stipulated conditions for testing a given lot of one component (cardiolipin or lecithin) of the antigen used in a given serological technique might be stated briefly as follows, except that there may be more than one such system of tests that a lot must pass for complete acceptance :

(1) We are considering a universe U of all possible observations that can be made in a given manner, each observation consisting of a " test " of a given specimen using a completely accepted (reference standard) antigen preparation, and a like " test " of the same specimen, using a like antigen preparation, except for use of the lot in question of the given antigen component.

(2) The universe is considered as infinite. It is possible instead to deal with the case of a finite universe ; the needed relations have been given elsewhere, [77] but this involves greater difficulty in construction of needed tables. The observations are considered as a random sample from U.

(3) We adopt a criterion whereby each observation (results of the indicated pair of " tests "), is unequivocally classified in one or the other of two categories ; for convenience in discussion these are called defective observations and non-defective observations, respectively. We let n denote the number of observations (pairs of " tests ") thus made in a stipulated manner with the particular antigen-component lot in question ; let a denote the number defective and b denote the number non-defective ($n = a + b$). Furthermore, we let ϕ denote the unknown relative frequency of non-defective observations in the universe U ; ϕ may be considered as the limit of b/n as $n \longrightarrow \infty$.

(4) If we knew the value of ϕ, we could stipulate some number p and agree to accept the lot if $\phi > p$, otherwise to reject it. This being impossible, we compromise by stipulating two numbers ($p' \leq p''$) and agree to accept the lot if the risk is not more than α that $\phi < p'$, and to reject the lot if the risk is not more than β that $\phi > p''$, where α and β are stipulated risk-tolerances.

(5) If we take $p' < p''$ a decision to accept or to reject will be reached within a definitely limited amount of sampling ; i.e., for some $n \leq n_o$ which depends upon p', p'', α and β. This is always true.

(6) We can construct a table of numbers n'_a and n''_a such that, for any given value of a, the conditions for acceptance are satisfied if $n \geq n'_a$, those for rejection if $n \leq n''_a$.

Note. This is always possible ; although the initial computations in making the table for use may be difficult, its use is simple. Thus, define $n' (a, \alpha, p) \equiv n'$ such that $I_p (n'-a, a + 1) \leq \alpha < I_p (n' - 1 - a, a+1)$ in terms of the incomplete beta-function ratio extensively tabulated by Pearson.[63] Then, appropriate interpretation of relations [72] as elsewhere indicated [48, 73, 74, 77, 78, 79] shows that the required critical values of n for a decision are given by : $n'_a = n' (a, \alpha, p')$ and $n''_a =$ the greatest n such that $I_{p''} (n-a+1, a) \geq 1-\beta$.

These and other systems of direct-probability sequential analysis can be shown to yield a decision in accordance with the stipulations at the earliest opportunity. A complete table has been constructed for the case $p' = 0.75$, $p'' = 0.85$, and $\alpha = \beta = 0.02$; and, likewise, for the case $p' = 0.975$, $p'' = 0.995$, and $\alpha = \beta = 0.02$. The values found for n_o were 267 and 536, respectively. The tables were prepared in accordance with the stipulations adopted by Maltaner and Maltaner for test systems employing " reacting " and " non-reacting " sera, respectively, in complement-fixation tests. [47, 48]

SUMMARY

The compounding of cardiolipin antigens requires preparation of pure cardiolipin and lecithin. Both substances may be prepared from beef-heart ; however, since egg lecithin is more easily purified than other lecithins, its use in antigens is recommended.

Minced beef-heart is extracted successively with acetone and methanol and the methanol extract is precipitated with barium chloride. After separation of the barium precipitate, lecithin may be precipitated from the filtrate with cadmium chloride.

The barium precipitate contains cardiolipin, which is purified by a series of fractionations of the salts of sodium, barium, and cadmium. The final product is a dehydrated ethanol solution of the sodium salt. The various steps which have been described in previous publications are here combined in a form which has been proved satisfactory in repeated use. It is emphasized, however, that other methods of purification may be equally satisfactory if they are shown to lead to the same final product.

Lecithin is best prepared by cadmium chloride precipitation of an ethanol extract of fresh egg yolks previously defatted with acetone. The precipitate is purified by : (1) repeated precipitation of a chloroform solution with ethanol containing cadmium chloride ; (2) separation from 80 % ethanol saturated with petroleum ether ; (3) removal of cadmium and treatment of the free lecithin with a 4 : 1 mixture of ether and acetone at 3°-6°C to remove ether-insoluble matter. The same general procedure may be used to purify lecithin from more complex sources such as beef-heart, but a greater number of steps is needed. In either case the final product

RÉSUMÉ

La préparation d'antigènes à base de cardiolipine exige l'emploi de cardiolipine et de lécithine pures. Ces deux substances peuvent être préparées à partir du cœur de bœuf ; cependant, il est recommandé d'utiliser la lécithine d'œuf, plus facilement purifiable que les autres lécithines.

Le cœur de bœuf haché est épuisé successivement par l'acétone et le méthanol, puis l'extrait méthanolique est précipité par le chlorure de baryum. Après séparation de ce précipité, on peut précipiter la lécithine en ajoutant au filtrat du chlorure de cadmium.

Le précipité de baryum contient la cardiolipine, dont on opère la purification par fractionnements successifs, sous forme de sels de sodium, de baryum et de cadmium. Le produit final est une solution du sel de sodium dans l'éthanol absolu. Les diverses opérations qui ont été décrites dans des publications antérieures sont ici combinées, sous une forme qui, à l'usage, s'est révélée satisfaisante. Cependant, il est rappelé que d'autres méthodes de purification peuvent être considérées comme adéquates si elles permettent d'obtenir un produit final d'égale qualité.

Pour préparer la lécithine, la meilleure méthode consiste à ajouter du chlorure de cadmium à un extrait éthanolique de jaunes d'œufs frais, dégraissés par l'acétone. Le précipité ainsi formé est purifié par : 1) précipitation répétée d'une solution chloroformique par du chlorure de cadmium dans l'éthanol ; 2) séparation à partir de l'éthanol à 80 % saturé par de l'éther de pétrole ; 3) élimination du cadmium et traitement de la lécithine libre par un mélange de quatre parties d'éther pour une partie d'acétone, à 3°-6°C de manière à éliminer les substances insolubles dans l'éther. La même technique générale peut être appliquée à la purification de la

is a dehydrated ethanol solution of free lecithin.

The final solutions are analysed for nitrogen, phosphorus, iodine number, dry weight of solute, and in the case of lecithin, for amino-nitrogen. Details for the determination of phosphorus, iodine number, and dry weight are given.

Serological as well as chemical tests are required to determine whether new lots of cardiolipin and lecithin compare satisfactorily with reference standard lots. Both complement-fixation and flocculation tests are used. An antigen mixture is prepared according to a previously determined formula, the new lot being used instead of the corresponding reference-standard component ; this antigen is compared with one composed entirely of reference-standard materials, in such a way as to show whether stipulated conditions of agreement between them are met.

Directions are given for comparing antigens in the two tests officially used by the New York State Department of Health. The text includes only such portions of these procedures as are needed for evaluation of antigens ; it is not intended as a complete manual for serodiagnostic use.

The principles of the complement-fixation test have been discussed in numerous publications ; the details of technique here presented include simplifications and modifications adopted as a result of recent experience. The antigen formula is : cardiolipin 0.0175%, lecithin 0.0875%, cholesterol 0.3%.

Two groups of sera, defined as " non-reacting " and " high-titre ", are selected in a one-tube screening-test with the standard antigen. For each group, conditions are stipulated for rejection and for tentative acceptance of an antigen-com-

lécithine d'origine plus complexe, telle que celle de cœur de bœuf ; les opérations sont alors plus nombreuses. Dans l'un ou l'autre cas, le produit final est une solution de lécithine libre dans l'éthanol absolu.

On détermine, sur les solutions finales de cardiolipine et de lécithine, la teneur en azote, la teneur en phosphore, l'indice d'iode, le poids du résidu sec ; pour la lécithine, on évalue, en outre, la teneur en azote aminé. L'article donne des précisions sur la détermination du phosphore, de l'indice d'iode et du poids du résidu sec.

Il est nécessaire de contrôler au moyen de tests sérologiques et chimiques la qualité des lots nouveaux de cardiolipine et de lécithine en les comparant avec des lots de référence. A cet effet, on recourt aux réactions de fixation du complément et aux réactions de floculation. On prépare, selon une formule préalablement établie, un mélange antigénique dans lequel l'échantillon à examiner remplace le composant antigénique-étalon correspondant. Ce mélange est comparé à un antigène composé uniquement de substances-étalons, de façon que l'on puisse se rendre compte si le nouveau lot satisfait aux exigences prescrites.

L'article donne des indications pour la comparaison des antigènes au moyen des deux épreuves employées officiellement par le New York State Department of Health. L'auteur expose seulement celles des opérations qui sont indispensables à l'évaluation des antigènes, et ne prétend pas présenter un manuel complet de leur application au séro-diagnostic.

Les principes de la réaction de fixation du complément ont été discutés dans de nombreuses publications ; les détails techniques figurant dans cet article portent sur les simplifications et des modifications auxquelles ont conduit des expériences récentes. La formule de l'antigène est la suivante : cardiolipine 0,0175%, lécithine 0,0875%, cholestérol 0,3%.

On constitue — sur la base d'une épreuve unique effectuée par rapport à l'antigène étalon — deux groupes de sérums, les uns « non réactifs », les autres « de titre élevé ». Pour chaque groupe on établit des critères de rejet ou d'admission

ponent lot in question, tests being made with the reference-standard antigen in parallel by the respectively prescribed technique. Observations with each group are made in a serial manner, and a system of direct-probability sequential analysis is applied to yield a decision, to accept or to reject, at the earliest opportunity according to the stipulated criteria. These are based upon experience with the respective technique as indicators of satisfactory behaviour of antigens in subsequent use in corresponding sero-diagnostic tests ; changes in technique or in tolerances of error might require corresponding changes in the criteria for decisions. Detailed directions and tables are given to facilitate the application. The fundamental ideas involved in direct-probability sequential analysis are discussed briefly in an appendix.

provisoire du composant antigénique soumis à l'examen. Des épreuves parallèles sont effectuées avec le composant antigénique-étalon, selon les techniques respectives indiquées. Dans chaque groupe les observations sont faites en série ; on applique un système d'« analyse séquentielle de probabilité directe » (direct-probability sequential analysis) afin de déterminer, le plus tôt possible, le rejet ou l'admission de l'échantillon d'après les critères fixés. Ceux-ci sont établis empiriquement et sont valables pour chacune des techniques respectives. L'expérience a montré qu'ils permettent de déterminer les antigènes donnant des résultats satisfaisants lorsqu'on les utilise ensuite pour les réactions de séro-diagnostic correspondantes. Des changements apportés à la technique ou aux marges d'erreur admises peuvent exiger la modification de ces critères. L'article contient des directives détaillées et un certain nombre de tableaux qui facilitent les déterminations. Quant aux éléments fondamentaux de la méthode dite « direct-probability sequential analysis », ils sont discutés brièvement dans une annexe.

The antigen for the slide flocculation test has the formula : cardiolipin 0.03%, lecithin 0.3%, cholesterol 0.9%. The test is performed on a paraffin-ringed slide, rotated, and read promptly under a microscope. Results are expressed as −, ±, +, 2+, 3+, or 4+. Photographs typical of these degrees of reaction are given as an aid in reading. High-titre sera are tested in serial dilution in salt solution ; the titre is defined as the highest dilution to give a 2+ reaction.

L'antigène utilisé pour l'épreuve de floculation sur lame a la formule suivante : cardiolipine 0,03%, lécithine 0,3%, cholestérol 0,9%. Cette réaction est exécutée sur une lame portant un anneau de paraffine ; la lame est soumise à un mouvement de rotation et aussitôt examinée au microscope. Les résultats sont exprimés selon la notation : −, ±, +, 2+, 3+ ou 4+. L'article est accompagné de photographies caractéristiques qui représentent ces différents degrés de réaction, et peuvent servir de guide dans la lecture des résultats. S'il s'agit de sérums de titre élevé, l'épreuve est effectuée sur des dilutions en série dans la solution physiologique. On désigne comme « titre » du sérum la dilution la plus élevée donnant une réaction 2+.

Test and standard antigens are compared by simultaneous tests on each of 3 days with 10 non-reacting, 10 low-titre, and 10 high-titre sera, also with a single pool

Les antigènes à l'examen et les antigènes-étalons sont comparés simultanément à l'aide de réactions effectuées chaque jour pendant 3 jours successifs avec 10 sérums négatifs, 10 sérums de titre peu élevé et 10 sérums de titre élevé, ainsi qu'avec un mélange de ces derniers, en dilutions.

of high-titre serum used in dilution. No statistical method of evaluation has been devised for this test, but conditions of agreement between two antigens based on experience with the technique are stipulated.

Aucune méthode statistique d'appréciation n'a été mise au point pour cette épreuve, mais des conditions de concordance entre les deux antigènes ont été fixées d'après l'expérience acquise dans l'utilisation de cette technique.

———

BIBLIOGRAPHY

1. Almeida, J. O. (1950) *Hospital, Rio de J.* **37**, 847
2. Andujar, J. J., Anderson, M. M. & Mazurek, E. E. (1948) *Amer. J. clin. Path.* **18**, 199
3. Arnold, R. C. & Mahoney, J. F. (1949) *J. vener. Dis. Inform.* **30**, 217
4. Bohls, S. W. & Shaw, P. (1948) *Amer. J. clin. Path.* **18**, 253
5. Brown, R. (1944) *J. Bact.* **47**, 581 *(Soc. Proc.)*
6. Brown, R. (1945) *J. Bact.* **49**, 199 *(Soc. Proc.)*
7. Brown, R. (1946) *J. Immunol.* **52**, 17
8. Brown, R. (1946) *J. Immunol.* **53**, 171
9. Brown, R. (1947) *Amer. J. Syph.* **31**, 304
10. Brown, R. (1948) *Amer. J. clin. Path.* **18**, 565
11. Cordier, P. & Sexe, H. (1949) *Rev. franç. Sérol. Chimiot.* No. 5, 107
12. Elek, A. (1928) *J. Amer. chem. Soc.* **50**, 1213
13. Faure, M. (1949) *Bull. Soc. chim. biol.* **31**, 1362
14. Faure, M. & Coulon, M. J. (1948) *Bull. Soc. chim. biol.* **30**, 533
15. Giordano, A. S., Culbertson, C. S. & Higginbotham, M. W. (1948) *Amer. J. clin. Path.* **18**, 193
16. Giordano, A. S., Frost, R. J. & Higginbotham, M. W. (1949) *Amer. J. clin. Path.* **19**, 25
17. Harris, A. & Portnoy, J. (1944) *Vener. Dis. Inform.* **25**, 353
18. Harris, A., Rosenberg, A. A. & Del Vecchio, E. R. (1948) *J. vener. Dis. Inform.* **29**, 72
19. Harris, A., Rosenberg, A. A. & Riedel, L. M. (1946) *J. vener. Dis. Inform.* **27**, 169
20. Hinton, W. A. (1948) *J. vener. Dis. Inform.* **29**, 27
21. Hinton, W. A., Stuart, G. O. & Grant, J. F. (1949) *Amer. J. Syph.* **33**, 587
22. Kahn, R. L. (1949) *Amer. J. clin. Path.* **19**, 61, 347
23. Kahn, R. L. et al. (1946) *Univ. Hosp. Bull., Ann Arbor*, **12**, No. 9, 81
24. Kahn, R. L. & McDermott, E. B. (1948) *Amer. J. clin. Path.* **18**, 364
25. Kahn, R. L. & McDermott, E. B. (1948) *J. Lab. clin. Med.* **33**, 1220
26. Kent, J. F., Boyd, H. M. & Sanders, R. W. (1948) *Bull. U.S. Army med. Dept.* **8**, 284
27. Kent, J. F., Culwell, W. B., Coatney, G. R. & Cooper, W. C. (1948) *J. Lab. clin. Med.* **33**, 747
28 Klein, S. J. & Leiby, G. M. (1948) *Amer. J. Syph.* **32**, 377
29. Klein, S. J., Leiby, G. M. & Berke, M. (1948) *Amer. J. clin. Path.* **18**, 940
30. Kline, B. S. (1946) *Amer. J. clin. Path.* **16**, 68
31. Kline, B. S. (1948) *Amer. J. clin. Path.* **18**, 185
32. Kline, B. S. (1949) *Amer. J. clin. Path.* **19**, 598
33. Kolmer, J. A. (1949) *Amer. J. med. Technol.* **15**, 293
34. Kolmer, J. A. & Lynch, E. R. (1948) *J. vener. Dis. Inform.* **29**, 166
35. Levin, W. (1949) *Rev. franç. Sérol. Chimiot.* No. 5, 88
36. Levine, B., Kline, B. S. & Suessenguth, H. (1948) *Amer. J. clin. Path.* **18**, 212
37. Lundbäck, H. (1949) *Nord. Med.* **42**, 1826
38. McDearman, S. C. & Cottrell, J. E. (1949) *Amer. J. clin. Path.* **19**, 156
39. McDermott, E. B. & Kahn, R. L. (1948) *J. Lab. clin. Med.* **33**, 1224

40. McDermott, E. B. & Kahn, R. L. (1949) *Univ. Hosp. Bull., Ann Arbor*, **15**, 93
41. Mahoney, J. F. (1948) *Amer. J. clin. Path.* **18**, 230
42. Mahoney, J. F., Zwally, M. R. & Harris, A. (1947) *Publ. Hlth Lab.* **5**, No. 5, 2
43. Maltaner, E. & Maltaner, F. (1935) *J. Immunol.* **29**, 151
44. Maltaner, E. & Maltaner, F. (1945) *J. Bact.* **49**, 199
45. Maltaner, E. & Maltaner, F. (1945) *J. Immunol.* **51**, 195
46. Maltaner, E. & Maltaner, F. (1946) *J. Immunol.* **54**, 253
47. Maltaner, E. & Thompson, W. R. (1948) *Application of direct probability sequential analysis to acceptance or rejection of antigens for complement-fixation tests for syphilis* (Research report, 11 May)
48. Maltaner, F. & Thompson, W. R. (1948) *Annual report of the Division of Laboratories and Research, New York State Department of Health*, p. 32
49. Merrill, M. A. et al. (1949) *Publ. Hlth Lab.* **7**, 2, 16
50. Muraschi, T. F. & Tompkins, V. N. (1949) *Amer. J. clin. Path.* **19**, 152
51. Niederl, J. B. & Niederl, V. (1942) *Micromethods of quantitative organic analysis*, 2nd ed. New York, p. 199
52. Pangborn, M. C. (1941) *J. biol. Chem.* **137**, 545
53. Pangborn, M. C. (1941) *Proc. Soc. exp. Biol., N.Y.* **48**, 484
54. Pangborn, M. C. (1942) *J. biol. Chem.* **143**, 247
55. Pangborn, M. C. (1944) *J. biol. Chem.* **153**, 343
56. Pangborn, M. C. (1945) *J. Bact.* **49**, 199 *(Soc. Proc.)*
57. Pangborn, M. C. (1945) *J. biol. Chem.* **157**, 691
58. Pangborn, M. C. (1945) *J. biol. Chem.* **161**, 71
59. Pangborn, M. C. (1946) *Fed. Proc.* **5**, 149
60. Pangborn, M. C. (1947) *J. biol. Chem.* **168**, 351
61. Pangborn, M. C. (1948) *Rev. franç. Sérol. Chimiot.* Nos. 3-4, 70
62. Pangborn, M. C. (1951) *J. biol. Chem.* **188**, 471
63. Pearson, K., ed. (1934) *Tables of the incomplete beta-function*, Cambridge
64. *Physician's Bull.* 1949, **14**, 34
65. Price, I. N. O. & Wilkinson, A. E. (1950) *Lancet*, **1**, 14
66. Rein, C. R. & Bossak, H. N. (1946) *Amer. J. Syph.* **30**, 40
67. Rein, C. R. & Kostant, G. H. (1949) *Arch. Derm. Syph., Chicago*, **60**, 217
68. Shaw, P. D. (1948) *Amer. J. med. Technol.* **14**, 7
69. Silliphant, W., Engelfried, J. J., Ellis, G. S. & Butterfield, B. (1949) *U.S. nav. med. Bull.* **49**, 995
70. Thompson, W. R. (1933) *Biometrika*, **25**, 285
71. Thompson, W. R. (1935) *Amer. J. Math.* **57**, 450
72. Thompson, W. R. (1936) *Ann. math. Stat.* **7**, 122
73. Thompson, W. R. (1947) *Annual report of the Division of Laboratories and Research, New York State Department of Health*, p. 35
74. Thompson, W. R. (1948) *Bull. Amer. math. Soc.* **54**, 288
75. Thompson, W. R. (1948) *Use of recursion formulas to extend tables of the incomplete beta function ratio.* In : *Annual report of the Division of Laboratories and Research, New York State Department of Health*, p. 33
76. Thompson, W. R. (1948) *Extension of tables of the four-variable psi function.* In : *Annual report of the Division of Laboratories and Research, New York State Department of Health*, p. 33
77. Thompson, W. R. (1949) *Annual report of the Division of Laboratories and Research, New York State Department of Health*, p. 27
78. Thompson, W. R. (1949) *Hum. Biol.* **21**, 17
79. Thompson, W. R. (1950) *Science*, **112**, 449
80. Thompson, W. R., Rice, C. E., Maltaner, E. & Maltaner, F. (1949) *J. Immunol.* **62**, 353

81. Ulrich, C. A. & McArthur, F. X. (1942) *Amer. J. clin. Path. (Tech. Suppl.)*, **6**, 84
82. United States Army Medical Department (1948) *Bull. U.S. Army med. Dept.* **8**, 247
83. Van Slyke, D. D. (1929) *J. biol. Chem.* **83**, 425
84. Vogelsang, Th. M. (1948) *Acta path. microbiol. scand.* **25**, 167
85. Vose, L. O. (1949) *Publ. Health Lab.* **7**, No. 5, 108
86. Wadsworth, A. B. (1947) *Standard methods of the Division of Laboratories and Research of the New York State Department of Health*, 3rd ed. Baltimore, Md., p. 361
87. Wadsworth, A., Maltaner, E. & Maltaner, F. (1931) *J. Immunol.* **21**, 313
88. Wadsworth, A., Maltaner, F. & Maltaner, E. (1938) *J. Immunol.* **35**, 105
89. Wadsworth, A., Maltaner, F. & Maltaner, E. (1938) *J. Immunol.* **35**, 217
90. Widelock, D. (1948) *Amer. J. clin. Path.* **18**, 218
91. World Health Organization, Expert Committee on Venereal Diseases (1949) *Off. Rec. World Hlth Org.* **15**, 18 ; *Bull. World Hlth Org.* **2**, 139
92. Yasuda, M. (1931) *J. biol. Chem.* **94**, 401

WORLD HEALTH ORGANIZATION
MONOGRAPH SERIES

No. 1.

PSYCHIATRIC ASPECTS OF JUVENILE DELINQUENCY

Lucien BOVET

1951, 90 pages, price 5/- $1.00 Sw. fr. 4.—
Separate editions in English and in French

No. 2. ## MATERNAL CARE AND MENTAL HEALTH

John BOWLBY

1951, 179 pages, price 10/- $2.00 Sw. fr. 8.—
Separate editions in English and in French

No. 3. ## LUTTE ANTIPALUDIQUE
PAR LES INSECTICIDES A ACTION RÉMANENTE

E. J. PAMPANA

1951, 72 pages, price 5/- $1.00 Sw. fr. 4.—
· French edition only

No. 4. ## EXPERIMENT IN DENTAL CARE
RESULTS OF NEW ZEALAND'S USE OF SCHOOL DENTAL NURSES

John T. FULTON

1951, 87 pages, price 5/- $1.00 Sw. fr. 4.—
English edition only

No. 5. ## ATLAS OF FRAMBOESIA

Kenneth R. HILL
R. KODIJAT
M. SARDADI

1951, 52 pages, price 5/- $1.00 Sw. fr. 4.—
English edition only

No. 6. ## CARDIOLIPIN ANTIGENS

Mary C. PANGBORN   *T. BEECHER*
F. MALTANER   *W. R. THOMPSON*
V. N. TOMPKINS   *Mary Rose FLYNN*

1951, 64 pages, price 5/- $1.00 Sw. fr. 4.—
English edition only

No. 7.

THE COST OF SICKNESS AND THE PRICE OF HEALTH

C.-E. A. WINSLOW

1951, in preparation
Separate editions in English and in French

No. 8. ## KWASHIORKOR IN AFRICA

J. F. BROCK
M. AUTRET

1951, in preparation
Separate editions in English and in French

bind
fam

WHO publications may be ordered, directly or through your usual bookseller, from the following agents:

ARGENTINA
Editorial Sudamericana, S.A.
Calle Alsina 500
BUENOS AIRES

AUSTRALIA
H. A. Goddard Pty, Ltd
255a George Street
SYDNEY

BELGIUM
Agence et Messageries de la
Presse, S.A.
14-22 rue du Persil
BRUSSELS

BOLIVIA
Librería Científica y Literaria
Avenida 16 de Julio 216
Casilla 972
LA PAZ

BRAZIL
Livraria Agir
Caixa Postal 3291
RIO DE JANEIRO. D. F,

CANADA
The Ryerson Press
299 Queen Street West
TORONTO, Ontario

CHILE
Edmundo Pizarro
Merced 846
SANTIAGO

CHINA
The Commercial Press, Ltd
211 Honan Road
SHANGHAI

COLOMBIA
Librería Latina, Ltda
Apartado Aéreo 4011
BOGOTÁ

COSTA RICA
Trejos Hermanos
Apartado 1313
SAN JOSÉ

CUBA
La Casa Belga
René de Smedt
O'Reilly 455
HAVANA

CZECHOSLOVAKIA
Librairie F. Topič
Národní Třida 9
PRAGUE I

DENMARK
Librairie internationale
Einar Munksgaard
Nørregade 6
COPENHAGEN

DOMINICAN REPUBLIC
Librería Dominicana
Calle Mercedes 49, Apartado 656
CIUDAD TRUJILLO

ECUADOR
Muñoz Hermanos y Cía
Plaza del Teatro
Casilla 522
QUITO

EGYPT
Librairie " La Renaissance
d'Egypte "
9 Sharia Adly Pasha
CAIRO

FINLAND
Akateeminen Kirjakauppa
Keskuskatu 2
HELSINKI

FRANCE
Editions A. Pedone
13 rue Soufflot
PARIS, 5e

GREECE
Librairie internationale
" Eleftheroudakis "
Place de la Constitution
ATHENS

GUATEMALA
Goubaud y Cía, Ltda, Sucesor
5a Av. Sur, No 6 y 9a C.P.
GUATEMALA

HAITI
Max Bouchereau
Librairie " A la Caravelle "
Boîte postale 111-B
PORT-AU-PRINCE

INDIA
Oxford Book & Stationery Co.
Scindia House
NEW DELHI

IRAN
Bongahe Piaderow
731 Shah Avenue
TEHERAN

IRAQ
Mackenzie's Bookshop
BAGHDAD

ISRAEL
Leo Blumstein
P.O.B. 4154
35 Allenby Road
TEL AVIV

LEBANON
Librairie Universelle
BEIRUT

LUXEMBOURG
Librairie J. Schummer
Place Guillaume
LUXEMBOURG

NETHERLANDS
N. V. Martinus Nijhoff's
Boekhandel en Uitgevers
Maatschappij
Lange Voorhout 9
THE HAGUE

NEW ZEALAND
The United Nations Association
of New Zealand
1011 G.P.O.
WELLINGTON

NORWAY
Johan Grundt Tanum Forlag
Kr. Augustsgt. 7A
OSLO

PHILIPPINES
D. P. Pérez Co.
132 Riverside
SAN JUAN

SWEDEN
Aktiebolaget C. E. Fritzes
Kungl. Hovbokhandel
Fredsgatan 2
STOCKHOLM 16

SWITZERLAND
Librairie Payot, S.A.
LAUSANNE, BÂLE, BERNE,
GENEVA, MONTREUX, NEU-
CHÂTEL, VEVEY, ZÜRICH
Librairie Hans Raunhardt
Kirchgasse 17
ZÜRICH 1

SYRIA
Librairie Universelle
DAMASCUS

TURKEY
Librairie Hachette
469 av. de l'Indépendance
ISTANBUL

UNION OF SOUTH AFRICA
Van Schaik's Bookstore (Pty)
Booksellers and Stationers
PRETORIA

UNITED KINGDOM
H.M. Stationery Office
P.O. Box 569
LONDON S.E.1

**UNITED STATES OF
AMERICA**
Columbia University Press
International Documents Service
2960 Broadway
NEW YORK 27, N.Y.

URUGUAY
Oficina de Representación de
Editoriales
Prof. Héctor D'Elía
18 de Julio 1333 - Palacio Díaz
MONTEVIDEO

VENEZUELA
Escritorio Pérez Machado
Conde a Piñango 11
CARACAS

YUGOSLAVIA
Državno Preduzeče
Jugoslovenska Knjiga
Maršala Tita 23/II
BELGRADE

Orders may also be addressed to

WORLD HEALTH ORGANIZATION

Sales Section, Palais des Nations, Geneva, Switzerland